Never Say Excuse Me Louder Than You Burp

Growing Up In Middle America

Bob Deaton

Bob Deaton

Twelve O'Clock Press
Huntington Beach

Published and Distributed in the United States by:
Twelve O'Clock Press
PO Box 1336
Huntington Beach CA 92648

ISBN 0-9768578-0-4

Library of Congress Control Number: 2004012345

Twelve O'Clock Press books are available at quantity discounts for bulk purchases. For more information please contact info@twelveoclockpress.com.

First Printing June 2005

10 9 8 7 6 5 4 3 2 1

I dedicate this book to Maria, Jeremy and Tara, who are always there to remind me that life is too important to take seriously.

acknowledgements

So many people came to me like angels with just the right help at just the right time. Thanks to you all for believing in this project and for being cheerleaders or schoolmarms, as needed. I want to express my gratitude to Lenny Burdette for his graphic design and typography critique, to Susan Burdette for her proofreading help, to Jack Beckwith for his fine-tooth comb, to Carol Bourgey for her enthusiasm, and to Holly Miller and Guy Adams for their encouragement.

I would particularly like to thank my family – Jeremy for his insightful and unvarnished editing, Tara for asking me to read my book to her friends, and Maria for her endless patience and support.

Finally, I send my special thanks to Mom, Dad and Tom for providing me such a rich source of material and teaching me the importance of humor in my life.

contents

preface

Everything in this book is true except for the parts that aren't. It happened just like this. And if it didn't, it could have, because somewhere between our memories and the facts lies the truth. The truth is that a girl named Debbie stood in front of Miss Beck's first grade class on a spring day in 1953 and emptied her bladder. I remember. I was in the Splash Zone.

At my thirtieth high school class reunion in 1995 I met up with a classmate I remembered from grade school, Debbie Clamp. She stood next to me in a crowd posing for the class picture, and we struck up a conversation.

"Hey, Debbie," I said jovially. "Remember that time in first grade when you were standing up in front of the class and peed on the floor?"

"That didn't happen," she answered brusquely.

The photographer demanded smiles and Debbie gritted her teeth, but I kept talking in dogged pursuit of her lost memory.

"Yeah, it was you. I remember you were standing right in front of me, and you told Miss Beck that you couldn't hold it any longer. You must have dropped about a quart. I'm not surprised you couldn't hold it."

"I told you that wasn't me," she said with considerably more indignation than I had expected. The statute of limitations had run out after all, and she would not be compelled to confess to the principal or do hard time in the after-school prison.

"I'm pretty sure it was…"

The photographer flashed and Debbie shot me a withering look that she'd been cultivating since our meeting.

"Hey, wait a minute," I said. "You're right! It was Debbie *Gifford*, not you!"

But it was too late. She vanished more quickly than the spots in front of my eyes, and I have not seen her since. Somehow the two Debbies had melded into one in my mind, but it was now clear that there was the Debbie who had peed on Miss Beck's floor and the one who had not.

To protect all the Debbies of my youth from the embarrassment of an occasional fuzzy memory, an indiscreet truth, a deliberate detour into the woods or the more imaginative recollections of my junior prom, the reader should assume that the characters and events in this book are fictitious. Even Debbie.

introduction

In the Eisenhower years the baby Jesus made an appearance on the courthouse lawn every Christmas in our Indiana town, wrapped in swaddling clothes and crying for a diaper. We burned trash in fifty-five gallon drums out in the alley, and any kid with a quarter could score a pack of unfiltered Luckies from a vending machine when no one was watching. Once a year the Coca-Cola guy came to our elementary school and parked his big red truck up on the playground. All pretenses of learning were suspended so that each of us could enjoy six and a half ounces of the Elixir of Life. Dogs roamed leash-free to forage and fight and copulate and form packs and establish hierarchies, and aside from TV and retirement plans, they were just like everyone else in Middle America.

I grew up right next door to hell – a Shell station, really. Every now and then the *S* in its overhead sign would fail, and my friend Mikey and I would laugh wickedly at the big red lights of HELL burning in the night sky, and we'd say *hell* right out loud and hardly get in trouble with our moms like we usually would.

Driving across the long black hoses in the driveway of the *HELL* station always set off a *ding-ding-ding* that signaled a crew of highly trained men in spiffy uniforms to swarm out and make love to our car and dispense their product for 29.9 cents a gallon. Armed only with paper towels and a spray bottle, one of the swarm spread the bugs around the windshield to a uniform translucence, while another conversed with Dad in a language only the two of them shared. *Buckaregular!* Dad would say, to which the leader of the swarm would reply *Checkyerall?* Dad would nod his assent, and the hood of our '51 Hudson would raise before us, concealing the highly skilled hands groping the mysteries that lay beneath. The car would turn its head and cough, and Highly Skilled would reveal a dripping stick, proclaiming *Squartlow!* and Dad would reluctantly dig another quarter out of his pocket and add it to the dollar in his hand.

Across the street at the Standard station Ella Jo Sipes and her weasly boyfriend sneaked off to the men's restroom for afternoon trysts. Little Jody was conceived, they say, right beneath the sign that urged customers to inform the attendant if they were not completely satisfied.

Beyond the gas station was the city swimming pool where on Tuesdays from 9:00 AM to 11:00 AM the unwashed masses were admitted for free. All other times it was a dime for kids and twenty-five cents for adults, who would have rather eaten raw pork than trusted their well-being to the miracle of chlorine in a public bath. Each summer day the air was filled with the delighted squeals of the bathers and the ashes that belched freely from the smokestacks of the water-works and settled over our clotheslines like Black Death. A handful of smokestacks was visible from our backyard, and I always carried the notion that criminals were dropped down those smokestacks as a consequence of their crimes, only to end up as soot on the white shirts that I wore to Sunday school.

Adjacent to the swimming pool was the fairgrounds, annual site of the Fabulous Anderson Free Fair, where nothing was free except the heady aroma of cotton candy and sweat. A quarter could get you a live chameleon on a string or two minutes of diesel-powered mechanized rotational terror in The Bullet. Within vomiting distance of The Bullet were the marvelously opaque White River and the Ninth Street Bridge, which connected us with the glamour and excitement of downtown Anderson.

Beneath the bridge old colored men fished for carp with cane poles. The river flooded now and again. In 1913 its muddy water invaded the house, reaching the mantles above the fireplace. A flood threatened again in 1957, but the levee held that time. Our cellar did fill with water on several occasions, and each time it left the air thicker than an Egyptian tomb, adding to my suspicions that the cellar was haunted for sure.

Across the bridge and beneath the railroad tracks was the passageway to downtown. It was in this tunnel that I encountered the F-word for the first time, painted in clean strokes in a hand far neater than my own and used in a perfectly grammatical sentence. Despite my unfamiliarity with the word, I sensed that it was bad. Very bad. Still, I appreciated the artistry of the writer. Graffiti is not what it used to be.

Beyond the tunnel were all the things of importance during my adolescence. There was Dr. Boski's chamber of dental horrors, where amidst the scent of cigars and clove oil even the first-time patient could enjoy countless hours of fear and pain for no money down. A few blocks beyond was Anderson High School, conveniently located next to that halfway house we knew as Central Junior High School. On the same campus was The Gym. Masquerading as a facility to serve the physical education needs of both schools, it was in fact an 8500-seat shrine to Hoosier high school basketball, where prayers were fervently offered up in the waning moments of close games, and half were answered.

Down the street was the First Methodist Church, where prayers were also submitted with a comparable rate of return. God lived downtown – there was no Second Methodist Church that might have distracted Him – and on weekdays He made the occasional visit to our side of the river. The church hosted a wedding nearly every Saturday except during basketball season, which was a blackout period unless the bride-to-be was certifiably pregnant. Even then, the ceremony was performed reluctantly and was poorly attended.

The ritual was always the same. The betrothed arrived at church as man and woman. The bride promised to obey. Each of the dearly beloved gathered there together exercised the *forever hold your peace* option, and the couple exited as man and wife. We dearly beloved retired to the basement of the church with the man and his wife, where our patience was rewarded with punch and cookies. We watched on with mock interest as the bride and groom opened their gifts and squealed in mock delight as the paper and ribbon gave way to one toaster after another.

We wondered with real, albeit sordid, interest whether the bride's newfound voluptuousness was wedding day radiance or because she was bursting forth with child. In the months to come, when the eight pound "preemie" made its appearance, the grownups found great sport in counting the months backwards and clucking their tongues. After the presents and the cake, it was over. No dinner, no dancing, no tacky garter ritual. Just punch and cookies and one gleaming chrome toaster after another.

Aside from the ever-pervasive threat of nuclear annihilation, life was simple. TV was black and white only, just like our town, and there were two networks, NBC and CBS. Later on, the upstart ABC network would appear on channel thirteen, broadcasting snow most of the day. Meals were simple variations of meat, potatoes, white bread and vegetables, which were boiled to safe and benign pastel versions of their raw form. Our palates were teased by a variety of spices, ranging from salt to pepper.

There was one authentic ethnic restaurant in Anderson, a Chinese place specializing in chop suey. Vouching for its authenticity were the chopsticks inscribed with real Chinese characters that came with every meal. They were utensils, it was rumored, though no white person in Anderson was known to be versed in their usage, and it was doubtful that any colored person had ever been inside the restaurant.

When my great-grandfather built our sixteen-room house down by the river in the 1890's, it was queen of the neighborhood. With the advent of the automobile, though, came the arrival of the Shell station next door, and the neighborhood began its long downhill slide, so gradual we could scarcely notice. Neighbors moved in and out before I could learn their names. Many had bad taste in music, and when advances in audio technology made it possible, they played it at offensive volumes. There seemed to be more spit flying in the air, too, including my own. The gentile Hoosier milieu apparent in Mom's old photo albums was no longer there, but then real life never comes in sepia.

Each evening after delivering twenty-five miles of mail, for which the U.S Post Office collected three cents a letter, Dad napped peacefully on the front porch of our big yellow house on the chaise lounge he had built from plans in a 1952 issue of *Mechanix Illustrated*. The chair was all nails and wood and sharp edges, and no one could sit on it except Dad – not that he minded, but because it hurt. He was impervious to pain, though, and watched the sun go down from that chair every summer evening. He was a reclining man in a declining neighborhood. I didn't sit there much, but Nancy Ann Petersen gave me my first kiss in that chair when I was five and that didn't hurt a bit.

Tree-ripping storms with wind and rain and Judgment Day lightning battered our house each spring and summer. On many a stormy night, Mom dragged my brother Tommy and me down to the southwest corner of the cellar, secure in the knowledge that when the tornado ripped our house from its foundation, the only survivors would be those wise enough to have sought safety there. The severity of the storms always made me temporarily forget about the resident spiders and ghosts there in the cellar, but when the threat subsided, I couldn't wait to get back to bed.

Dad was a believer in neither the southwest corner nor the cellar ghosts and valued his sleep too much to be bothered about something as inconsequential as Armageddon. Grandma and Great-Aunt Martha were out of Mom's sphere of influence, and trusting great-grandpa's construction, they rode out the storms in the comfort of their own beds. Tommy, who was nine years older than me, opted out as he grew up, mocking Mom's blueprint for survival. When I became of age I followed Tommy's precedent, also substituting mockery for self-preservation.

Mom abandoned her cellar strategy when it appeared that she would be the only survivor and instead prayed for us from beneath her covers. She prayed us out of many disasters, confirming that God did make visits to our side of the river. Of course, if a tornado had left us in splinters, that too would have been an Act of God. It didn't do to be on God's bad side.

I could tell you more, and I intend to. The accounts that follow are seemingly random strokes from the palette of life in Middle America, but when viewed at a distance through the foggy lens of time, they comprise an impressionistic image of a childhood that is both universal and uniquely mine. Wipe your feet, come on in and stay for a while. And close the door behind you.

oscar gets a cleaning

I remember the day that Mom wasted Oscar. She cooked him up in the oven and gave me his charred remains as a keepsake. Claimed it was an accident. People were like that in the 1950's. I was four.

Oscar and I, we went everywhere together, fighting off wolves and conspiring against the bogeyman in the basement. We spied on my brother and considered the possibility of intelligent life after 9:00 PM. Was Clarabelle really mute, we wondered, or just jerking Howdy Doody around? Like Clarabelle, Oscar wasn't much of a talker. He was a heck of a listener though. Stuffed rabbits are like that. He was the best friend a kid could have.

Somewhere along the way Oscar had picked up a protective coating of filth, a dingy layer of experience that came from being dragged everywhere I went for two years. Oscar refused to walk, but he would always accept a drag if one were offered.

As any mother can tell you, dirt-encrusted rabbits rank just below toilet seats and doorknobs in their ability to carry disease. And so it was that Oscar met his fate. To save me from the imminent onset of smallpox, polio and stuffed rabbit fever, Mom captured Oscar while I was napping and cleaned him. She nonchalantly delivered the toasted vestiges of his body to me as if nothing had happened.

A field of short brown stubble, which bore an uncanny resemblance to Vice-president Nixon's five o'clock shadow, had replaced Oscar's once-luxuriant snow-white coat of down. And he smelled like a casualty in a poultry processing plant meltdown.

"What happened to his fur?" I whimpered. "It's all burnt off!"

"I washed him for you and put him in the oven to dry, and, um, he stayed in there too long."

Now wasn't that just like Oscar to stay in the oven too long? The oven had served as the crematorium for family dinners often enough that Oscar really should have known better.

"Well, he stinks!" I cried, holding him up for Mom to sniff. "And he looks like Nixon!"

I regarded Oscar's face in growing horror. "What happened to his eyes?" I shrieked.

Where once there were delightful little button eyes that gazed at me in wonder, there were now only blackened threads, pathetic excuses for optic nerves.

"I took them off. I was afraid you'd eat them."

Two years past my oral fixation phase and here Mom was, ripping the eyes out of my bunny!

I gave Oscar back to her, never to see him again. I like to think I became a man that day, gaining the instant maturity that comes from innocence lost.

But then Mom got me a stuffed bear with delightful little button eyes and saggy jowls, and I named him in memory of Oscar.

Nixon and I, we went everywhere together.

first kiss

Nancy Ann Petersen and I had kissed no more than a dozen times before I talked her out of her T-shirt. It was one of those languid July mornings in Indiana where the air itself was an aphrodisiac, and we were alone on the front porch. Nancy Ann was my neighbor and we had been together on the porch about a million times, but this time she was in unfamiliar territory. It felt good to be waist-up naked, as long as the bugs stayed away, but Nancy Ann didn't share my enthusiasm. Instead, she put her shirt right back on and ran home, mumbling something about what her mother had always told her. That was the first and only occasion on which we kissed. She kissed me good, too, and I liked it. I was five, and so was she.

Mom had hosed off the front porch earlier that day, and the fresh smell of the damp concrete conspired with the honeysuckle to make me temporarily crazy, crazy enough to want to kiss Nancy Ann. I didn't even like playing with

Nancy Ann, Nancy Ann and her stupid girly games, but kissing her suddenly seemed like a good idea. I lay on the tortuous wooden lounger that Dad had built and devised my strategy.

"I'll pretend to be asleep," I said, "and you do something to wake me up, okay? Something with your lips."

"Want me to whistle?"

She attempted a whistle, but the only sound was air.

"Huh-uh. Do something else."

"I can blow spit bubbles! Wanna see?"

Nancy Ann churned up a mouthful of spit and let loose a string of bubbles, a foamy replica of Niagara Falls – from the Canadian side.

"No, that won't make me wake up," I said, although I was impressed. "Think of something else."

"You want me to kiss you?" she snickered.

"Yeah," I snickered back. I closed my eyes to see what might happen, and she did it. Right on the lips, too. She surprised us both, I think, but I kept my presence of mind.

"I'm still asleep," I said.

She came at me once more, raining down kisses on me – sometimes I could be a very sound sleeper – but she bored of our game long before I did and stopped. That's when we got our shirts off. It meant nothing to me, our stripping to the waist. It was a hot day, and I was simply extending her the courtesy of becoming one of the guys. And without her shirt there was nothing there to suggest that she wasn't one of the guys. Nancy Ann was having none of it though, and ran for home as fast as a kid pulling on a T-shirt possibly could. Girls. Who could figure them out?

Soon after our escapade I began to suspect that my brother had seen us. Tommy had learned to play a new song on the piano with the simple yet unmerciful lyrics "Bobby's got a girlfriend, Bobby's got a girlfriend..." The second verse was the familiar "Na-na-na-na-NAA-na", but he usually just stuck to the first. Over and over and over he played until I reached a state of sufficient fury to pummel him with ineffectual blows. He was a fourteen-year old giant and impervious to my attacks. When he'd had enough, he'd either swat me away with a well placed smack or rat me out to Mom.

"Mom! Bobby's hitting me!"

"Bobby, stop hitting Tommy."

"But Mo-o-om! He's playing that song again!"

"What song?"

At this point I had to tread lightly. I dared not describe the "Bobby's Got a Girlfriend" song by name, lest she press me for details. I knew I would crack under her questioning and offer up particulars that I preferred to keep to myself. All I needed was for Mom to broadcast to all our friends and relatives that her five-year old son was making out with a neighbor girl, and right out on the front porch in broad daylight, no less. No, I would omit the embarrassing minutiae and press my case with just the essential facts.

"You know – that SONG!"

"Try to get along with your brother, Bobby. And Tommy?"

"Yes, Mom?" Sometimes he was such a choirboy.

"Don't."

"Don't what, Mom?"

"I don't know. Just don't."

Mom disappeared and Tommy resumed the concert, no lyrics, no chords – just the soft relentless one-fingered strains of the melody. I ran away, but there was no escape. The music had lodged in my mind like blood on Lady Macbeth's hands. I vowed never to kiss Nancy Ann again or even play with her if that's what it took.

It was a dozen years until my next kiss. It took me that long to find a girl as indiscriminate as Nancy Ann Petersen. And to get that song out of my head.

* * *

A year or so had passed since I'd made out with Nancy Ann Petersen on the front porch. We still played together from time to time, but there was no encore episode, nor was there any special little place in my heart reserved just for her. Other girls became a growing source of fascination for me though, and in my imagination no female outside the immediate family and not yet on Social Security was safe from my lips.

I knew that it was wrong to be kissing Nancy Ann or anyone else outside of wedlock, at least not without dinner and a movie first. Kissing and thinking about kissing were both wonderful wellsprings of guilt. I had vowed that Mom and Dad would never find out about Nancy Ann, and I was hoping that God had not noticed either. For now, Mom was the bigger threat as God's earthly agent of morality and humiliation. I was skating on the thin ice of deception, but I was still on the up side of the ice – until the night Mom blind-sided me with a shot from out of nowhere.

"Bobby, have you ever kissed a girl?"

"No!" I fired back, generously slathering on all the disgust that I could muster. I put my face down in the water and held my breath for seven or eight minutes, maybe longer, but when I came sputtering to the surface she was still there. She bought my answer though, and I skillfully guided the conversation to something less consequential.

"So, Mom, how about that Korean War, huh?"

I didn't like lying to Mom. I'd never done it before and I felt awful, but I managed to put the whole kissing caper safely behind me. Or so I thought, until Nancy Ann brought me back to reality.

"You know those tiny white flecks you get on your fingernails?" she said one day.

"You mean these?" I held out my hands for inspection. My nails looked like the war memorial in the park at the height of pigeon season.

"Yeah, those. You get those from telling lies."

"You do?" I gulped.

"Uh-huh. Boy, you have a lot of 'em!"

I did have a lot of them. How could that be, I wonder quick action I'd be wearing the scarlet *K* T-shirt, but what could I do? Painting my nails was no option. Wearing gloves in the summertime would raise too many questions. I briefly considered pulling my nails out one by one and blaming Tommy, but that wouldn't work either. Mom always took his side. Always.

Then in one of those eureka moments that come only once or twice in a lifetime, the solution came to me. I'd lie my way out of it. Not a big lie this time – just big enough to get the job done, an innocuous lie that I could cite when she saw the sad state of my nails. Brilliant, yes. Cunning and devious, too.

The perfect opportunity to execute my plan arose on Sunday. A fib on the Sabbath would count double and explain the army of flecks amassed on my fingertips. It was our custom on Sunday evening to gather up in the living room around the old black and white Fada with the bad vertical hold and watch the *Disneyland* television show. The big hand on the clock was racing toward twelve, but Mom was upstairs, not in her customary position on the davenport. Soon fireworks would be bursting in spectacular black and white over Sleeping Beauty's castle. At two minutes until eight I stood at the bottom of the stairway and delivered up to Mom the second lie of my life.

"*Disneyland's* on!" I shouted, knowing full well we'd first have a hundred and twenty seconds of Buicks, Lucky Strikes, Extra-strength Anacin and, ironically, Mr. Clean. I savored the peace of mind my little deceit had brought me, and Mr. Clean wrapped it up with his hearty baritone promise "to ed. I'd only told one miserable lie, but I guess it was a whopper, by the looks of what my conscience had disgorged on my fingernails. Mom would surely be onto me now. Without clean your whole house and everything that's in it."

I inspected my nails for telltale changes as Mom walked in, just in time for the first salvo over Sleeping Beauty's castle.

"Did I miss anything?" she said.

"Not a thing, Mom," I said, slipping my hands into my pockets. "Not a thing."

five easy pieces

"What'll it be tonight, Bobby? Chiffon cake or vanilla ice cream?"

"Aspirin, Mommy, aspirin! I want St Joseph's Aspirin for Children!"

Mom never went for that, of course, even if it was my favorite dessert. If I wasn't cooking along at 102 or better, I could forget the aspirin. Still, St Joseph's was orangey good and better than candy. It made fevers worthwhile – the mere sound of Peggy Lee's voice made me salivate – and it almost certainly was an excellent source of vitamin C.

I took the thermometer from its hiding place in the credenza. I admit it. Knives, matches, rat poison and the power saw were all more accessible and would have been safer playthings, but it was the thermometer that compelled me. I slipped it under my tongue, confident that I could break 102 as an act of sheer will.

"Look, Mommy! I can take my temperature!"

I bit down hard on the thermometer to keep it from sliding away and snapped it in two at the hundred-degree mark. What I lacked in technique at the age of five, I made up in raw energy. Mom carefully removed half a thermometer from my mouth and looked in horror at the silver liquid pooling there. Her expression suggested that I had done something ... regrettable. Amidst the rich, crunchy goodness of shredded glass, I detected a foreign flavor. Mercury, was it? What better complement to a serving of glass shards than mercury?

Mom immediately sprang to action, phoning the neighborhood pharmacist to confirm her worst fears. Doctors apparently weren't to be bothered late in the day.

"If that's mercury in there," he said, "he's out of luck. Let me check it out, and I'll call you right back."

While we waited for the pharmacist's call, Mom rushed me into the bathroom and offered the only words of comfort at her disposal.

"Go in there and throw up!"

I closed the door behind me and quickly locked it. Vomiting on demand was going to be tough enough without an audience.

"Are you doing okay, Bobby? Are you throwing up yet?"

"Uh, just about!"

I surely did not want to die, but even less did I want to vomit. I stared at my reflection in the toilet water and waited for a miracle to rise up from within me. But none rose.

"Open the door, I want to come in."

Instead of opening the door, though, I gagged and retched long and boisterously, mixing in groans to nice effect. I took care to select only vomiting groans from my repertoire and omit any that might be confused for the sounds of succumbing to poison. To cap off a superb presentation I spat heartily into the toilet, flushed and announced in triumph that I could not throw up one bit more.

For my convincing performance in the bathroom, Mom rewarded me with a brand new jigsaw puzzle. I don't know where the puzzle had come from. Maybe she kept it on hand for just such an occasion, the way some mothers keep Ipecac. It was remarkably uninteresting as jigsaw puzzles go – just a puppy chasing a ball, except the smile on the puppy's face was unnaturally cheerful in a way that disturbed me. And it had only five pieces. With so little time left on my clock, Mom probably figured that a puzzle with more parts would have been wasteful. Long before the mercury had time to eat its way through my bowels, I had mastered the puzzle and set it aside. The wonder and mystery of a five-piece puzzle fades fast.

"Do not induce vomiting" was not a warning label we saw in the 1950's. Those were primitive times, and we believed in purging the poison from our bodies before it killed us. Now the labels advise us to skip the barfing and immediately consult a physician, who is uniquely qualified to assess the direness of our straits and prescribe the appropriate puzzle. When time is running out, it's still the classic five piece grinning dog. Slower acting food poisoning might get you a two hundred-piece puzzle of, say, *The Last Supper*. Puzzles like these were once commonplace, but are now scarce and available by prescription only.

Soon the pharmacist called back with good news – I was out of the woods. The thermometer contained alcohol, not mercury. He recommended that I rest and avoid driving and operating heavy machinery for the next four to six hours. Mom melted into relief, maybe she cried. I don't remember. I was not too happy though. It was straight to bed for me with no playtime on the jigsaw, no St. Joseph's Aspirin for Children, and nothing to comfort me but a five-piece puppy with a creepy smile.

amen and pass the chicken

"Bobby, would you like to return thanks?"

"No." I waited in vain for someone else to step forward, but no one did. I was eight, and saying grace was a fate that always befell me as the youngest in our family. Couldn't we once just skip the preamble and get right to the fried chicken?

"Why doesn't Tommy do it? He never does it!" It was true. My seventeen-year old brother had long since graduated from dinnertime prayer duty.

"Because," Tommy jumped in, "the Bible tells us that 'Blessed are the little children, for they shall say grace at dinner.' That's you."

"It does not ... does it?"

I looked around the table to see everyone nodding in solemn agreement. Tommy struck a reverential pose, head bowed, hands folded, waiting for me to begin.

"Look," I suggested, "couldn't we just go by the grocery and bless the food once and get it over with? It would save us lots of time."

"Bob-BEEE!"

The menace in Mom's eyebrows sent me a very clear message. I was flirting with blasphemy. I had defied Mom from time to time, and offended God as well, but doing both at once was not a risk I was willing to take. This praying job was mine. Fortunately, this was an infrequent task that I had to endure only when we had company or when Mom was in a particularly spiritual mood and required me as her personal spokesman to the Almighty.

I ran through my stock prayer on autopilot as fast as I thought I could get away with, making sure to complete it in a single breath, while keeping one eye on my brother lest he try to slip the drumsticks onto his plate while I was communing with God. For effect, I always inserted a reverential one second pause before the *amen*. I'm convinced that that one-second pause saved me from many requests to do it again, only slower.

> *Thank you for the world so sweet,*
> *Thank you for the food we eat,*
> *Thank you for the birds that sing,*
> *Thank you God for everything*
> *… And please help me not to wet the bed tonight.*

The tag line wasn't standard mealtime faire, but a rider I threw in as part of my bedtime ritual, as long as I had God's attention. I can't say that He was all that helpful about keeping me dry, but He did grant me the remarkable ability to sleep peacefully through anything – drought, drizzle or downpour. I rushed immediately to amen without the usual one-second pause, hoping no one would notice my *faux pas*.

"Pass the chicken please," I said with an air of great immediacy.

My ploy failed, of course. Everyone did notice my bed-wetting request, and Mom in particular took it as a source of great merriment. I made it a point to omit that line from my bedtime prayer that night, ensuring that I would be surfing by morning and Mom would be changing my sheets as penance.

Mom was undeterred by my spotty climate control and persisted in her requests that I say grace. She relished the possibilities of bloopers in my prayers, I believe, and was willing to accept my solemn supplications to the Almighty with an occasional side order of the ridiculous. With no younger siblings behind me in the pipeline, I continued to be the returner of thanks for the family. My assignment persisted until finally I broke the bedwetting habit and Mom decided it would be just fine for us to be thankful on our own time, pass the chicken please.

At the other end of the spiritual spectrum was dinner at Grandma's house. She dished out a magnificent meal of fried chicken, mashed potatoes, green beans drenched in bacon grease and dinner rolls the size of volleyballs, *and* she did all the praying herself. Her prayers always ended with the phrase "Bless this food for its intended use," which I interpreted as "Bless this food, for it's in tendon juice." This curious twist always gave the impression that it was a prayer of petition designed for a blowfish cook, rather than a prayer of thanks. "Dear Lord, please protect us from the tendon juice with which I have prepared this meal, for without Your divine intercession we shall surely die. Amen."

I, for one, was a believer in the power of prayer, at least during my waking hours, and I was always the first to call out in a demonstration of my faith.

"Pass the chicken, please!"

attacking the wagon train

In the dark days of 1955 there was no Cartoon Network, no Nickelodeon, no Disney Channel. There were no VCRs, DVDs or video on demand. Nor was there electronic saturation bombing of young Americans naively called "kids", but now more rightly identified as the "children age five-to-nine living in households with televisions" demographic. There was no way for me and my friends to plug into a TV and satiate ourselves with children's programming like lab rats guzzling cocaine. In my small Indiana town there was just Saturday morning TV for my demographic and me, and much of that was swill.

Before the broadcasters rolled out of bed on Saturday morning my day at the TV trough began with the WFBM test pattern, a black and white graphic of an Indian chief in profile. Despite its low entertainment value, I stared at that image until it was burned into my retinas and visible everywhere I looked. The pre-dawn TV Indian also moved my neighbor Mikey, because every Saturday morning at sunrise he burst through his back door screaming "Attack wagon train!'" Finding no wagon trains, he would return to his standard you're-too-close-you'll-go-blind viewing position twelve inches from the set and stare at the Indian until the official TV day kicked off with a non-denominational prayer, sixty seconds of uninspired programming with even less entertainment value than the test pattern.

Mikey was my cartoon buddy, and our tastes ran to more violent faire, Mighty Mouse in particular. Mighty Mouse's tremulous voice belting out "Here I come to save the day" was an inspiration for all in my demographic. Mikey and I never tired of watching him vanquish his archenemy Oil Can Harry week after week. We aspired to have theme songs of our own one day, but until then, this one would do just fine.

We had our occasional fights, Mikey and I – nothing violent, just name-calling and saber rattling – but it was understood that a truce would be in effect by 10:30 AM on Saturday morning. This was doubly true if the television at his house or mine was out of order. Mighty Mouse was powerful but no match for a stubborn vertical rectifier or horizontal disambulator.

Mighty Mouse could have been every mother's worst nightmare – consider a vermin with the strength of a bull and capable of supersonic flight – but he spoke impeccable English and sang with good tone and decent relative pitch. Fortunately for Mikey and me, he was also a real Boy Scout, an all-American mouse. In truth no episode ever revealed him to be thrifty, clean or reverent, but we assured out moms that indeed he was, and they bought it. Sadly, he was outlasted by Mickey, a mouse with no special powers but enough connections and political savvy to survive while greater cartoon characters fell by the wayside.

Mikey was content with attacking wagon trains from dawn until dusk, but I was drawn into the world of comic books where the air was always rife with possibility. They were not the dark brooding gothic works of today with their heavy metal, uvula-pierced following. For a dime, a comic served up a half hour of entertainment. Every panel was a visual snack and stirred my imagination like no TV show. I devoured them all from *Superman* a.k.a. Kal-el, son of Jor-el and Lara, to *Little Lulu* and her politically incorrect friend *Tubby*.

Superman succeeded where the TV Indian had failed. By the time I was seven I had wrecked my vision between the pages of those comic books, and glasses became a permanent fixture on my face. I was Clark Kent without the big red *S* on my chest, a pasty white worm with ribs and pipe cleaner arms. My meatless frame might have bought me valuable time in a Donner party scenario, but I was far from the Man of Steel ideal. Lucky for me that the answer was right there, smack in the middle of every volume of *Archie* comics.

"Send me a dime, and I'll send you a new body!" Charles Atlas shouted from the ad. "The World's Most Developed Man" had been a ninety-seven pound weakling when a bully at the beach kicked sand in his face and popped him on the chin for good measure. Atlas was humiliated, and his girl, a comely young miss out with him on a pity date, left him in disgust. His grave self-esteem issues and ninety-seven pounds of angst inspired him to develop a radical new exercise regime that left him with the body of a Greek god and a thriving worldwide bodybuilding business.

I was thirty pounds short of ninety-seven, but I could definitely claim weakling status. "Yes, Charles!" I cried out. "Give me a new body!" I sent in my dime, but Charles never wrote back, not even to say thanks. By the time I hit ninety-seven pounds I was a jiggling pear of a boy, not the scrawny weakling pictured in the ad. For years I considered complaining to the FTC, but technically I did have a new body. It was not until I was twenty that I regained my original scrawny proportions. Thanks all the same, Charles.

Alongside Charles Atlas was the inevitable ad for White Cloverine Brand Salve. The ad was really more about opportunity than salve. Sell the salve, it said, and win a pony! How much salve was required, it did not say. I assumed a good faith effort of ten or twelve tins would have me looking for a saddle and pony bed in no time. Mom and Dad said something about having to buy enough salve to fill the Grand Canyon. They never did like ponies.

The ads never said exactly what the salve was for, and I presumed it had some sort of illicit adults-only purpose that couldn't be described in a comic book. Pony or no, I wouldn't be selling that stuff. Not a nice Methodist boy like me.

Mikey wanted a pony as much as I did, if not more, but he wasn't much of a reader and would never know about White Cloverine Brand Salve. One day Mikey and his friend Warren found a great hiding place upstairs and watched Mikey's big sister change her clothes. All her clothes. A kid like that would have no qualms about telling me the secrets of the salve, but he never got the chance. The secrets of the salve remain locked away forever, and Mikey remained oblivious to the lost opportunity. His quest was attacking wagon trains – he claimed to be one-third Cherokee Indian, after all – and he pursued it with a zeal better directed toward salve selling. In later years I came to believe that there was no salve, only salve distributorships. Filling the Grand Canyon with distributorships was quite another matter.

The summer of 1955 I was subjected to a week of Bible School. It was my firm belief that I should be no smarter or no more religious in September than I was in June, and I resisted education of all manner during this most sacred season. I didn't care if it was Chocolate School. Check my calendar – summer's blocked. Mom thought a stretch at Bible School would do me some good though, and coerced Mikey, who I suspect was her real target, to join me. Mikey was very un-Bible School-like, but went along anyway and sat in the same stuffy room with thirty other captive clock-watchers.

Each day at our mid-morning recess Mikey burst through the doors of the First Methodist Church commanding us all to attack whatever wagon trains could be found in the parking lot. There were no wagon trains, of course, only station wagons, and no one joined him in his attack. After a couple of days of this it was suggested to Mikey that perhaps "Attack Wagon Train" was not appropriate for Bible School. Mikey complied, and on day three he broke out of the church screaming "Bombs over Tokyo!" instead. On day four Mikey did not return.

With Bible School safely behind us Mikey and I reverted to our usual games of violence and aggression. The dogs in our neighborhood ran loose in those days, and the roaming packs would often break into fits of intra-mural fighting. It was great entertainment, and we stood close by, rooting for our own. It was better than professional wrestling. It was a canine smackdown with no holds barred, but no one ever got hurt. Mikey's dog Lollipop was a benign little spaniel mix who did not often make the mistake of taking part. To Mikey's dismay she was the ultimate conscientious objector. If the rest of the pack were the Harlem Globetrotters, she was the Washington Generals. We suggested that he rename her "Wait till next time," but he was not amused. Everything changed for Mikey the day his sister acquired Lex, an all-powerful German shepherd. Lex was the alpha dog from the outset and was not hesitant about reminding lesser dogs of their place in the hierarchy. With Lex in the picture dogfights were just no good anymore, except for Mikey, who wrongly presumed that Lex's status in the pack was somehow conferred upon him.

Tough as Lex was, it was Lollipop that proved to be the undoing of Mikey and his family. Lollipop believed, as dogs do, that all the world was her toilet, the Newby's yard next door in particular. The fence was no deterrent to Lollipop, who knew a prime dumping ground when she saw one. Unfortunately, Lollipop's preferred target zone was prime grazing land for Little Mary Newby, age two, whose shoes, and more often bare feet, were Nature's perfect poop magnets. Richard, Little Mary's daddy, did the responsible thing and took it up with Mikey's dad, Lee, who was a morose, nasty drunk, not easily persuaded by arguments of reason. Richard was a decent enough guy, recent to manhood and the prototypical sand-in-his-face weakling that Charles Atlas types disdainfully refer to as "Before." Richard "Before" Newby lacked my instincts about Lee and confronted him over the low chain link fence separating their very different worlds.

"Do you think you could keep your dog out of our yard, Lee? She poops over here, and Mary steps in it."

Asking a man to contain his dog in 1955 was just not normal and maybe unconstitutional, too. And Lee was not a man prone to conversation or negotiation.

"Maybe you'd like to step out in the alley and do something about it," Lee suggested. The air was pungent with testosterone.

"Maybe I would," Richard replied, and they were off to the alley where Lee knew how to settle differences.

I watched from a safe distance as they pummeled each other with their fists. Richard took a shot in the throat early on and fell to the ground, ending the battle. Mikey and I relished our games of violence, but this was the real thing, and it scared the hell out of me. I wanted nothing more than to stop the carnage, but in the end I was powerless and did nothing.

Mikey wasn't around to see the fight, and when we were together, it was never mentioned. His dad was no Oil Can Harry tying Little Nell to the railroad tracks. He was something much worse, a man who would beat up his neighbor in defense of his dog's right to poop wherever it pleased, whether Little Mary stepped in it or not.

Not long thereafter, Mikey's family moved to California. I promised Mikey's mom that I would write to him, but I never did. I missed him though. It was a good move for them, because in the Golden State there were millions of back yards for Lollipop to poop in and that many new prospects for Lee to beat up. Maybe there were even some real wagon trains for Mikey to attack, too. And when the wagon trains had the day off, there to the west was Tokyo, two thousand miles closer than before.

messin' with the tooth fairy

It was 1956 and I was among the hard-core unemployed. The official government statistics may have painted a rosy economic picture, but at the age of eight I was flying under their radar. Business opportunities were scarce for someone of my tender years. Pop bottles were worth a penny apiece, a dime for a six-pack if returned in the original carton. Wire hangers also went for one cent each, but only when the lady at the dry cleaner was in the mood to buy them back. Aluminum cans were still in the distant future. The snow shovel was too ponderous, and the power mower, according to Mom, was a fiendish mechanism whose sole purpose was to whack off my appendages and scatter them across the yard in a bloody mush. It had happened to that guy in Kokomo – the mulch did wonders for his camellias, they say – and it could happen to me. Mom was remarkable in her ability to cite examples of people who had come to bad ends pursuing innocuous activities that were of interest to me. I am almost certain that she'd heard of a kid in Indianapolis who had put his eye out with a marshmallow. We never turned our back on the mower, not even when it wasn't running.

The Tooth Fairy was where the real money was. She was more generous than the grocer, more reliable than the dry cleaner, safer than the mower – and I made money while I slept! A quarter for an incisor was not uncommon. Most of my baby teeth surrendered peacefully to sugar-dusted cake donuts or Clark bars and even into my toothbrush now and then. But if they didn't go willingly, higher rewards were possible. Chokers were good for fifty cents, a full dollar if I saw the white light and dead relatives. Trauma spelled economic opportunity, and I milked it for all it was worth.

"Uncle Joe came to greet me, Mom!" I cried, as I coughed up a bicuspid. "He was there to welcome me to The Other Side!"

"Uncle Joe's not dead, Bobby. He's living in Muncie."

Same thing, at least during basketball season, but the Tooth Fairy would be accepting no metaphors.

A complete set of baby teeth could earn me as much as twenty bucks, but six or seven was more realistic. Teeth were diamonds in my mouth, a precious non-renewable resource. All I needed was another source of production, and it would be Easy Street for me. Buying futures on my friends' teeth would have been a shrewd investment. Take my pal Mikey, for instance. He was six years old and already a master of instant gratification. He would have sold me an option on all his babies for under a buck. It was a strategy that required patience, though, and my supply of patience was even lower than my inventory of teeth. Like Mikey, I was a short-term investor, and teeth futures had no place in my portfolio.

Everything changed the day I found the cow tooth. The huge calcified mass lying there in that country pasture outside Anderson was more than a tooth. It was financial independence, because there were plenty more teeth where that one came from. Persuading the cows to part with them was a detail I'd work out later. The Tooth Fairy would surely be impressed with teeth of that magnitude. I was rich.

That night I carefully slipped the cow tooth beneath my pillow where the Tooth Fairy could not miss it. I considered a note of explanation, but dismissed that idea no sooner than I got it. She was the expert. Any explanation would have only been an insult to her intelligence. The tooth would speak for itself.

When morning came my pillow lay as flat as it had the night before, undistorted by the mound of riches I had expected. This could only be good news. No big lumpy pile of coins beneath my head could only mean big bills or a certified check, maybe even a key to a safety deposit box at an offshore bank. There would be no more dredging through the soggy remains of pancakes and Sugar Crisp for me, not when the tooth I recovered would get me no more than chump change. No sir, it would be Golden Goose eggs from now on, only without the giant. But no, in some horrible mix-up of fate nothing lay beneath my pillow but disappointment — disappointment, the cow tooth and a note from the Tooth Fairy. The note was neither a treasure map nor an account number. It was a rejection notice.

"Sorry," it said tersely. "I do not accept cow teeth."

Implicit in her tone was "... and don't try it again, Buddy!" As if to rub my nose in it, the Tooth Fairy had ingeniously impersonated the handwriting of my own mother! Beneath the note was the cow tooth, an investment that looked far less glamorous and smelled far more pungent than it had the night before.

The only reasonable course was to sell the tooth to Mikey for a nickel, but Mikey wasn't buying. He was interested only in getting rich quick, and waiting until morning for a return on his investment was out of the question. So, it was back to business as usual for Mikey and me, scavenging pop bottles and wire hangers. And the cows of Madison County, they breathed a collective sigh of relief.

the monster in the basement

"You can't go out," Mom said, taking up a position be-tween me and the doorway to freedom, "until you turn off the light in the basement."

Everyone knew the house was haunted, especially the basement, but no one would admit it. No one except Tommy, that is, who took special delight in feeding my paranoia.

"Will you go with me, Mom?"

"Nope. You left the light on, and you need to turn it off."

My friends waited just outside, not to play, but to witness my end. Mom was the warden, but she wouldn't be walking the last mile with me.

We called it a basement, but it was a cellar really. It had the musty ambience of a tomb, but none of the charm. Only occasionally would I venture down there, only in the com-pany of someone else and only in the daylight. Mom had once banished my colony of pet hamsters to the cellar, where their fragrance would be more appreciated, but without me to feed them they soon died of natural causes. Deprived of the

usual nuts and berries, they had experimented with canni-
balism but were unable to make a go of it. Things like that
happened down there.

It was a lazy summer day, and I had been playing in the
cellar with my chemistry set, mixing poisons and explosives. I
was perfectly safe though, because Mom and Grandma were
down there washing clothes, and the beast dared not show its
ugly head with grownups around. Soon, however, they
finished and left me alone – a very bad move. Not only was I
exposed to considerable peril from The Beast, but their
freshly washed clothes were now absorbing the pungent
aroma of my burning sulfur.

Now alone and afraid, I abandoned my experiments and
retreated to the safety of the surface, relieved to have cheated
Death once again. Mikey and a couple of the neighbor kids
were waiting there to play with me, but Mom was there to
thwart my escape.

"I'm waiting!" Her eyebrows fell into the dreaded vee-
shaped I-mean-it formation.

With my friends watching over me through the screen
door, I descended the treacherous stone steps to the mouth of
the cellar and flipped off the light switch. The switch was
poorly grounded, and on many memorable occasions 110
volts had coursed through my highly conductive body. But
this time I was lucky – Old Sparky had taken the day off. I
was on my way out the door, but once again Mom stood
between me and freedom.

"Not *that* light," she said. "The one in the back."

The one in the back! Mom had raised the stakes to the
limit. How many times must an eight-year old face Death in

one day? Desperately, I tried to enlist my friends in my mission into the Cellar of Doom, but to no avail.

"Come with me, Mikey," I pleaded. "Please!"

I didn't think he'd offer much protection. He was only six. But he was slower than me, and I thought he could buy me some escape time.

"Huh-uh!" he cried.

His head shook back and forth so vigorously that we could hear his cheeks rattle. The other kids were shaking their heads too, daring not let their eyes meet mine. They knew as well as I that untold evil lurked beyond those steps, and they wisely refused. Just as well, I thought. No sense chumming the basement with extra monster bait.

With considerable reluctance I set off to meet my destiny armed with no more than a 28 ounce Louisville Slugger, an anemic lightweight model bearing the autograph of some no-name utility infielder from the Kansas City A's. It wasn't physical harm I feared so much, as being scared out of my mind and spending the rest of my life strapped to a straight-back chair, drooling and catatonic. My expression of mindless terror would be the only indicator that untold demons played an endless game of handball with my battered psyche.

Carefully, I entered the basement, switching on Old Sparky at the bottom of the steps. With my heart racing like a bunny caught in the high beams I hurried to the dank recesses where the bare bulb hung above my chemistry set. Just as I reached for the chain, a hideous cackle filled the air. It was the sound of Pure Evil.

"Hee! Hee! Hee!" it shrieked. "HEE! HEE! HEE!"

All I know is that the next instant I was at the top of the stairs, and my feet had never touched the floor. Never. Not once. And before I could get my heart started again, there was Tommy, bounding up the steps of the cellar, unfrightened, unharmed and laughing hysterically. Despite her best efforts to the contrary, Mom too joined the merriment. Equal parts of anger and relief replaced my terror of a moment before.

Tommy was unrepentant, of course, and as the years passed I began to worry about the considerable bad karma he surely must have incurred. If what goes around comes around, then something big must be coming for him, what with all the interest accruing on his karmic debt.

Twenty-two years after the cellar incident, I had occasion to borrow his car. As it sat parked in front of my apartment, I was awakened at 3:00 AM by the sound of a mighty crash. From my window I could see that it was Tom's car. A close-up inspection revealed that it was surely totaled. As I walked around taking inventory of the damage, a specter appeared before me from out of the darkness and spoke to me these words of comfort.

"Worry no more about your brother," the specter said. No other words were necessary. His meaning was clear.

"You're even!"

giants

In a recurring nightmare the giant would come across the Ninth Street Bridge looking for me. I could hear his steps long before I saw him, and the sky above him grew angry as he approached. He was as ugly as he was ill tempered, and he was there to eat my bones. That much was obvious from his expression. On a bad night the giants came in pairs, crazed as English soccer hooligans, and they would tear up the house before devouring me. Beyond the realm of my dreams I never saw a giant, but they were out there all right, and they were looking for me. Where they hid themselves in the flatlands of Central Indiana I do not know. Maybe they were stealth giants. There were regular bogeyman sightings, two or three a week in my neighborhood alone, and at night we'd see an occasional vampire masquerading as a bat, but we never did see a giant. They were as sneaky as they were mean.

On my first camping trip when I was four years old, we took a guided tour of a cave. Near the end the guide pointed out a formation on the ceiling he called "The Giant's Frying Pan." It was unmistakable, and it was just my size, too.

"Run for your lives," I screamed, "before the giant comes back!"

My warnings went unheeded, and everyone in the group, including my family who should have known better, laughed in great delight. The petty fools! I could just see them running from the cave as the giant fried me up in a bucket of pure pork lard with a little okra. I hated okra almost as much as I hated giants.

"Thank God that kid was there!" they'd shout. "That could have been us!"

Fate smiled upon me that day though, for the giant never caught up with us.

*   *   *

It was quite unlike me to plant the magic beans, considering the likely consequences. I don't know where I got them, only that they were magic, and that whatever transaction took place did not involve the family cow – although we did have a cat that Mom would have gratefully traded for a handful of beans, magic or otherwise.

It was a warm summer afternoon, and the garden was lush where I planted the magic beans. While I waited, my mind clouded with visions of the Golden Goose, whose 24K eggs would be worth $35 per ounce on the open market. It wouldn't take too many eggs for me to clean out the toy department at Sears and Roebuck. Then Mom and Dad could squander the eggs that followed on food and gas and other such foolishness that grownups are prone to buy.

With the beans safely in the ground I turned myself in for the mandatory nap. When it came to naps there were no suspended sentences or time off for good behavior. It was the Total Sleep Reciprocity Exchange deal kids had with the grownups of the world. The afternoon naps the adults so craved were taken from them by their employers. Those naps, with nowhere else to go, were distributed among the children. Naps must never go unused, it was believed. It was like leaving food on our plates when there wasn't enough chop suey to go around in China. And so, while I used up the nap untaken by an hourly assembly line worker at the tire plant in Akron, the beans grew. And grew. And grew.

When I awoke and ran to the garden, I found not beans, but a great plant even taller than I was and reaching higher with my every gasp. It was a hollyhock, a lanky raggedy weed that in Indiana is sometimes mistaken for a decorative plant. Mom had doubted the magic of my beans and planted it while I napped.

With the clarity that often comes from sleeping on it, I could now see that the whole bean extravaganza was a bad idea. The trip up the beanstalk would leave me scratched and bleeding. The giant would awaken to the tempting aroma of my O positive and include me in his lunch plans. He would be mean and hungry and dumb, too, misrhyming *fum* with *American* just as he always had with *Englishman*. If I escaped at all, it would be without the goose. Never one to accept last minute invitations for lunch, I ran to the house to fetch my rubber hatchet, just one of the many creative playthings in my arsenal of toys.

"What are you doing?" Mom cried out.

I guessed that Mom still had hopes for the goose, but she was out of this deal. I hadn't traded *her* cow to get the beans. This was *my* beanstalk, and it was going down. I gave it a vigorous whack, then another, then a third, but the safety approved rubber hatchet failed to nick the stalk. I was certain that it was growing even while I chopped at it and that there was a giant up there impatiently waiting for the elevator down. Two more whacks and a mighty push brought the hollyhock to the ground, its stalk still intact and ready for transplant.

I looked to the sky in relief. There would be no giant in our backyard on this day. At that same moment I also realized that there would be no more nighttime visits to eat my bones, and on bad nights, demolish the house. That evening I would celebrate with a large helping of okra, fried to perfection in pure pork lard.

me and robert strom

Supermarkets had yet to arrive in Anderson, Indiana in 1955, and neither had supermarket tabloids. I never missed them though, not with sources like my seven-year old neighbor Mikey. I could always count on him to give me the real thing, straight up with no sugar coating.

"My cousin told me about this kid," Mikey said. "He was looking out his car window, and this truck drove by real close, and it tore his face off! It's true. My cousin told me about him. He doesn't have a face!"

"He was just looking out the car window?"

"That's right. And a truck drove by and tore his face right off. It got stuck to the truck, I think. And you know what else my cousin told me? There was this other kid – he was so smart his brain burned up! It's true!"

"His brain burned up? How did that happen?" I imagined some hapless prodigy doing long division in his head with four-digit divisors. That would be like playing with a loaded gun. While molten brains poured from his ears, his mother would admonish him to PLEASE keep those brains off his new shirt.

"I don't know how it happened," Mikey said. "It just burned up, that's all. It's true!"

The kid that lost the face-off with the truck I could put out of my mind, but not the one with the burning brain. It was a cautionary tale with my name on it. I was, after all, the best reader in Miss Hatfield's third grade class. I could name all the planets in order and the number of moons that orbited each of them. I could spell Schenectady in one breath, even if I didn't know what a Schenectady was. There was no doubt in my mind that I was the smartest eight-year old in the Free World, and now my brain was in peril. Despite my brother's assurances that I wasn't really all that smart, I clung to my belief and took care to keep my brain properly cooled when thinking hard.

The night I saw Robert Strom on television everything changed for me. Strom was the boy genius who ran the gauntlet three times on *The $64,000 Question* and picked up another $32,000 on *The $64,000 Challenge*. I watched as he took on insanely difficult questions about the physics of planetary motion and the dominant fusion processes for stellar interiors. They were speaking a language that, although English-like, was totally unfamiliar to me. My knowing that Jupiter had twelve moons no longer seemed quite so impressive. I was not the smartest kid on the planet, but at best a distant second. Disillusioning as it was, I was able to take comfort in seeing Robert Strom handle those questions with no apparent brain damage.

With all his attention devoted to astronomy I assumed that Robert Strom, like me, had wasted no time learning more mundane skills, like tying his shoes. I was the last kid in my class to acquire this expertise, but I attributed this to a lack of interest more than any sort of intellectual deficit. Even Mom's clever use of peer pressure failed to motivate me.

"Your cousin Kathy can tie her shoes, you know."

Kathy was nine days younger than me and, according to Mom's schedule, should not have begun shoe tying for at least a week after I had achieved mastery.

"Oh yeah? Well, Kathy's Mom lets her ride her bike in the street, you know."

The peer pressure approach worked no better for me than it did for Mom, and I was relegated to riding on the sidewalk until I got my driver's license. It was lucky for me that the state of Indiana required cars to be operated on the streets.

We were in a new grade school with a new gymnasium, and we could not step onto the polished hardwood surface without the proper footwear. Changing into gym shoes to protect our new basketball shrine was a regular ritual, and the kids took turns tying my shoes for me. I always thought that this was something of a privilege for them, like beating the chalk out of the erasers or emptying the pencil sharpener. I'm embarrassed to admit now that I was completely unembarrassed about my lack of shoe-tying acumen. If Velcro had been around then, I still would be unable to make a knot, at least one that could be undone.

Once I had learned the names of all the butterflies native to Indiana, I could give my attention to the shoe thing. My teacher patiently walked me through the steps while my classmates raced into their gym shoes.

"Okay, just twist the two ends together once. Got that?"

I'd had that part down pat for about three years. It was what followed that baffled me.

"Now make a loop. See how the rabbit goes around the tree and down the hole?"

"That's a tree? You told me to make a loop. Why didn't you tell me to make a tree?"

"It was a loop. Now it's a tree."

"And this was a shoestring and now it's a rabbit?"

"I think you're getting it. Now show me."

I wound the left string around the tree in my right hand, trying to forget that it had been a loop just moments before.

"Now what?"

"No, no. The rabbit wants to go around the tree the other way."

"Why? What's the rabbit know that I don't know?"

"The rabbit always goes counterclockwise."

"Even in the Southern Hemisphere?"

"Everyone's rabbit goes counterclockwise. If you want me to help you, your rabbit must go counterclockwise."

Defeated, my rabbit succumbed to social pressure and reluctantly went around the tree counterclockwise, like all the other rabbits. Hard as I tried, all I could see when I stared at my shoes was a lemming running around the tree, just like all the other lemmings, then jumping off the cliff.

"Okay, pull the loop through the hole and you're done."

"Loop? What happened to the rabbit? "

"Forget the rabbit. Just pull the loop and you're done."

I pulled on the loop and what was formerly the rabbit came along with it.

"I found the rabbit. He was right behind the loop."

She sighed in exasperation. "Would someone please tie Bob's shoes? We have to get to the gym."

I watched as my friend Mark did his magic, forming two perfect bows in mere seconds.

"How do you do that so fast, Mark? How do you remember all that stuff about loops and rabbits and trees?"

"Bob," he explained, "they're just shoestrings."

They were just shoestrings! It was a moment of epiphany, and when we got into the gym I sat there tying and untying my shoes over and over while the principal droned on about bicycle safety or the importance of regular brushing or maybe it was crop rotation. It was not important. I now knew that Jupiter had twelve moons *and* I could tie my own shoes!

Only one problem remained. I couldn't tell my right shoe from my left. This normally didn't present much of a problem. If I got them on backwards, it was a small matter to switch them. But that was before combat boots. Shoe designers were known to be a dangerous and sadistic lot, typically foreign and probably Communist. Their mission was to inflict the maximum possible misery on the freedom-loving feet of the women of America. Unable to improve on the spike heel they had devised as an instrument of torture the year before, they turned their attention to the minds and feet of America's youth. Paratrooper chic was in now, and no fashionable third-grader's footwear collection was complete without a pair of combat boots. Putting them on once in the morning with Mom's help and removing them once at night was a manageable sacrifice to be in style. They took a considerable investment in time, however – twenty minutes to lace and another ten to unlace, a half hour a day devoted just to getting my boots on and off. For the six months that I wore them I neither bathed nor brushed my teeth in the interest of time management.

In a coincidence of poor planning, I wore my boots to school one day, only to learn that it was a gym day. I adroitly slipped out of my boots and into my black Converse high-tops and tied them with disdain. Shoestrings were no longer a worthy opponent. Getting back into my combat boots was another problem though.

"How do I tell my right from my left?" I had asked Mom.

"Oh, just look at 'em." she said. "You can tell. Really. It will be easy."

I stared hard at the boots waiting for divine inspira tion. I turned the boots over, aligned them with my feet, waited for the gestalt to carry me and tentatively slipped one onto my right foot. It felt okay, so I tried the other. I devoted the rest of the afternoon to lacing and tying them. Just as the bell rang I finished, much to my satisfaction. My satisfaction was short-lived, however, when I stood up and took one awkward step, then another. My feet swung outward in huge, torturous arcs. On the wrong feet, my combat boots had become remedial shoes with their own agenda. My investment in time was too great to switch now, and I walked the six blocks home, unintentionally kicking the streetlights on my left and small children at play to my right. Every step I took was another painful reminder that my brain would not be self-combusting anytime soon.

day of the spanish rice

Park Place Elementary School was brand new, but it had the generic scent of all other schools, the scent of floor wax and institutional food, of textbooks and fear. Fear was served up fresh and hot each day Monday through Friday by Miss Lefebvre, the principal and chief enforcer of all that was correct and proper. The chevron captioned *Dieu et mon droit* on her door declared her belief in the Divine Right of Principals. There were constant rumblings of dissent, but no one openly challenged her authority. Not until The Day of the Spanish Rice, that is.

Miss Lefebvre regularly prowled the lunch tables to see that no crumbs, no matter how unsavory, went uneaten. The cafeteria served up the standard midwestern lunch fare. There was the usual meat product, battered and deep-fried, with a protective coating of gravy that would camouflage its origins and seal in the few nutrients that had been unable to escape. There were the garden vegetables boiled for our safety until they were devoid of color. The peas were distinguishable from the corn only by shape. The vegetables were typically infected with red toxic flecks of a condiment that was neither salt nor pepper, and hence foreign and suspicious. A dish cleverly designed to resemble mashed potatoes was a frequent visitor to our plates, too. The safe bet portion of the lunch was the slice of soft white bread with its generous dollop of butter and a half-pint of creamy whole milk. Fish sticks were an end-of-the-week staple in public schools to satisfy closet Catholics observing meatless Fridays. In practice though, no Catholics attended public school, favoring St. Mary's, where the fish was rumored to be quite good.

Miss Lefebvre was from the "Eat it or else" school of dining, except there was no "or else." To most kids the creamy asparagus spears were no more palatable than a plate of worms. Given a choice, they would rather have been tossed into a rose bush than put asparagus spears in their mouths. This, unfortunately, was not an option. Bringing in a peanut butter and jelly on Wonder bread from home was not an option either, since the cafeteria charter forbade competition, even if it came in a humble brown bag.

The number of basic food groups expanded and contracted throughout the twentieth century, topping out at seven in the 1950's. The cafeteria made sure that we were afflicted with a representative from each group in every lunch, so the likelihood of finding something unappealing was high. For that reason I went home for lunch where there was no particular penalty for leaving uneaten food on my plate. Tommy claimed that Mom used to admonish him to clean his plate, because people in China were starving. By the time I came along though, China had gone communist and cleaning our plates no longer mattered. Such conspicuous consumption exemplified the superiority of capitalism, and leaving vast quantities of food untouched on our plates became our patriotic duty. Miss Lefebvre, however, would not allow us to help win the Cold War, and the Evil Empire would thrive for years to come because of her and her kind.

On one of the rare occasions that I ate at school, my lunch was served with a great foul-smelling wedge of cheese, an unwanted delicacy that was said to have been aged to a rancid perfection outside in the trash bin. After everything edible was gone from my plate, I tucked the wad of cheese into my mouth between my cheek and gum, taking care to keep it at a safe distance from my discerning taste buds.

As we filed out of the cafeteria onto the playground, I kept the telltale bulge concealed beneath my hand, ready to explain it away as a toothache. When we reached the play-ground, I ran for the most remote corner and disgorged the cheese over the chain link fence onto the sidewalk. I rational-ized that the dairy group had been well represented by the carton of milk I had drunk, and the cheese would serve only to upset the delicate balance in this dance of the food groups in my body. My cheese joined a growing mound that in-cluded Tuesday's stewed tomatoes and Monday's macaroni. The compost pile had become an ad hoc group science project, and my fellow diners waited patiently behind me to make their contributions. I had avoided both vomiting and the wrath of Miss Lefebvre. It was a good day.

Others were not so fortunate on The Day of the Spanish Rice, the day that would change everything. Any dish that was likely to be distasteful to the Hoosier palate was given a foreign name and passed off as a delicacy. No matter how indiscriminate the Spanish might be about eating creatures that wash up on the beach in the dead of night, they would never eat a dish like Spanish rice. It was strictly a domestic affliction. The rice was flavored with ingredients not found in the common kitchen, except perhaps under the sink, and tinted red to deceive us. Every kid likes red food. Cherry Popsicles and strawberry ice cream are red. Vegetables are not. Red is safe, but Spanish rice was not.

Occasionally a kid would throw up at lunch, but the damage was manageable in Miss Lefebvre's book. After one such episode and in a state of severe pique, Mr. Simms, the janitor, confronted her. "Stop makin' 'em eat that stuff! I'm tired of cleanin' up their puke!"

Miss Lefebvre called him into her office for a closed-door conference to refresh his understanding of his job description. He emerged bloodied but unbowed and gained instant mythic hero status among the students. Miraculously, he kept his job. Otherwise, nothing changed. Not until The Day of the Spanish Rice, that is.

It began with Terry Donnely and his three grains of rice.

Miss Lefebvre hovered over Terry observing the remnants on his plate. "Finish your rice, young man." Miss Lefebvre demanded.

"But Miss Lefebvre, there's only three grains! And they're burnt!" he protested.

"I said FINISH IT!"

Terry moved the three grains around his plate while Miss Lefebvre watched on. If they ever made it into his mouth, it was a sure thing that they would be going over the playground fence to join my cheese.

Meanwhile Mary Picard was sitting next to him, eyes down, trying desperately to disappear. The full serving of Spanish rice remained on her plate. Try as she might to conceal it beneath her silverware and crumpled napkin, she could not sneak it in under Miss Lefebvre's radar. Terry's three grains were a misdemeanor, but this blatant disregard of policy was a lunchroom felony. Miss Lefebvre tapped her finger fiercely on Mary's plate.

"Are you trying to get away with something here, young lady?"

"No, Miss Lefebvre. I couldn't eat it."

"Because?"

"Because it was yucky…" she whimpered.

"Because it was yucky," Miss Lefebvre echoed sarcastically. "Would you like for me to take you back to the kitchen so you can tell the ladies who worked so hard to bring you a nourishing lunch that it was … YUCKY?"

"No, Miss Lefebvre." Mary was crying quietly now, and Miss Lefebvre drew close, so close that Mary could feel her hot breath on her face.

"Then finish … your … RICE!"

Mary was crying openly now, as she raised a forkful of the red-stained rice to her lips. Before she could get it past them though, a torrent of splashy chunks blasted out onto the floor, onto the plates of the adjacent students, and best of all, onto Miss Lefebvre. The generous helping of partially digested nourishment lovingly prepared by the hard-working lunch ladies in the kitchen now dripped from her hair and saturated the squared shoulders of her no-nonsense starched and pressed navy blue principal's dress.

At the next table was Nicole Ericson, known by all for her delicate stomach, joining in the vomitfest. Like a chain reaction that only atomic scientists had ever witnessed, vomiteers arose at every table in nauseated solidarity with Mary Picard. Spewing forth the Spanish rice and everything that had gone down with it, each one seemed to proclaim, "No, *I'm* Spartacus!" It was a magnificent triumph of human biology over draconian lunchroom rule, and those that vomited that day did so proudly.

The legend of The Day of the Spanish Rice grew with each retelling. After thoroughly cleaning the lunchroom, it was said, Miss Lefebvre was sent away never to return. Mr. Simms put down his mop and became the new principal by acclaim, and from that day on, instead of fish on Friday, the cafeteria served chocolate cake – two helpings.

A handful of eyewitnesses claimed that nothing much happened that day, no doubt the same bunch who would later claim that NASA faked the moon landing in a TV studio. A couple of kids threw up, they said, and Mr. Simms made some indiscrete remarks. Miss Lefebvre heard nothing, and that was all there was to it.

They had it all wrong, and I knew it. I wasn't there that day, not in person, but there are some things that you just know.

chocolate goo

Most red-blooded, God-fearing Americans consider ice cream a treat, a frosty delicacy to be savored to the last sticky dribble. Not me, not that I didn't have endless opportunities to acquire a taste for it. Every Sunday night I opened up like a python swallowing a water buffalo and shoveled in ice cream until I was full to the top and the accumulated icepack on my soft palate gave me a headache that lasted until Tuesday. Sunday after Sunday ice cream was the appetizer, the entree and the side dish. There were no admonitions to eat my peas, no pleas to just try the fish, no threats to finish the rice – I don't care if it is burnt. Nope, just ice cream. Ice cream for dinner every week was not kid paradise. It was the Schick treatment that would have even the most hardcore ice cream aficionado crying for spinach.

We were a committed vanilla family, week after monotonous week, with an occasional daring foray into butter pecan. I was an adult before I realized vanilla was a legitimate flavor like banana or peanut butter and not just the absence of some real essence. The vanilla ice cream was nearly always accompanied by what Mom and Dad referred to as "chocolate goo. " For me, butterscotch was the only real topping, a treat we too seldom enjoyed. My teeth hurt when I ate anything cold, so I always drizzled the goo onto the ice cream and whipped it into a soup, the nearer to room temperature the better. Dinner was one big sticky lukewarm dribble.

One particular Sunday evening we found ourselves well stocked in vanilla ice cream but lacking the requisite topping. Mom and Dad drove me to a nearby store with instructions to go in and not come out without a can of chocolate goo. Unable to find it stocked on the shelf, I resorted to asking for help from the guy behind the counter.

"Got any chocolate goo?"

He stared at me as if I'd dropped in from outer space.

"Chocolate what?"

"Chocolate goo!"

"What's that?"

"You know," I answered impatiently, "the gooey chocolate stuff you pour on ice cream!"

This guy just wasn't getting it.

"Chocolate goo!" I screamed.

"You mean chocolate syrup?"

"No-o-o-o, I mean chocolate *goo!*"

God, this guy was dense. Syrup was for pancakes. It was *goo* I wanted. Then from out of nowhere he pulled a familiar brown can with silver lettering.

"Is this what you want?"

"Yes, that's it!"

Now he was getting it. What took him so long? Then, for what was obviously the first time in my ten years of life, I read the letters on the can. C-H-O-C-O-L-A-T-E S-Y-R-U-P. Chocolate syrup! My mind slipped into overdrive, and I wondered just how many times I had said "chocolate goo," and to whom had I said it? My friends? My teachers? Not that cute girl who sat behind me in Social Studies, I hoped.

"Give me that can!"

I paid and escaped as quickly as I could. There was business to tend to in the car with Mom and Dad. My wrath was not well contained. Not only was this the night that I was cheated out of real food for dinner, I had embarrassed myself by asking for – no, demanding! – a fictitious ice cream topping.

"This is not chocolate *goo*," I hissed between clenched teeth. "It's chocolate *syrup!*"

I pointed to the telltale letters on the can, but to my great surprise Mom and Dad seemed well aware that it was chocolate syrup. They also seemed to take way too much delight in the way I'd just been skewered in the store.

For a long while I sat in stony silence, obsessing on the ugly turn of events. I had but one remaining hope for salvaging anything from this Sunday evening.

"We got any butterscotch goo?"

new bikes, expired ducks

We won a bicycle once, my duck and I. It was the grand prize in the first Pet Parade in the history of Anderson, and we won it. The parade committee figured that, except for the occasional dog fight, an endless stream of kids walking their fox terriers and dragging bowls of guppies along in their Radio Flyer wagons would be wholly uninteresting to the viewing public. Consequently, it was decided that costumes would be required for all entrants, pets included. The intent was to level the playing field, so that turtles could compete with the ocelots and hamsters with the iguanas. Fish owners were left at a costuming disadvantage, but I didn't care. It was me and the duck against the entire animal kingdom, and we were ready.

It was one of those steamy, oppressive Indiana summer days that made the cheerful grumpy, the grumpy intolerable and all of us sweat like pigs. I remember little about the parade, other than endlessly marching up and down the main streets of town. Mom had dressed the duck as Uncle Scrooge and me as Donald. The duck rode comfortably in a cage atop my wagon in a bed of Monopoly money but was wholly unconvincing in his role as Scrooge. In a very uncapitalistic fashion, he desecrated the currency upon which he rested with a steady stream of vomit. By the end of the parade he was up to his duck knees in a pungent papier mache of 20's, 50's and 100's.

The judges either overlooked my animal's suffering or embraced the mess as part of the color and pageantry of this inaugural Pet Parade and awarded me a shiny new 26" bicycle. I couldn't revel in the moment though, because I felt like the duck. Furthermore, the bike was five years too big for me and held no more interest than a combination washer/drier, although it would be easier to get home.

A couple of Coca-Colas and a rest on the front porch swing restored me to my pre-parade condition. The duck was not so lucky and expired later that day, but at least he had the decency to wait until the parade was over. We all gave thanks for that over his lifeless body. It was a valuable biology lesson we learned that day, that ducks can be counted among the animals that require water. I felt bad for him, but got over it quickly. He was more like livestock than a pet, which is why I called him "the duck", instead of, say, "Ducky."

Dad lowered the seat on my prize bike, but my legs dangled years away from the pedals. It was sleek and red and nice enough, I guess, but it had no character. It was an appliance of a bicycle. The bike went straight into the cellar, not to see the light of day again until midway through the Eisenhower administration.

In the intervening years I rode my little black bike with solid rubber tires and lusted after Tommy's bike, forty pounds of mechanical excellence. It was much like the cars of that era, a mammoth chromed monument to bad taste with every feature a kid could conceivably want – headlight, horn, speedometer, odometer – and it was massive enough to withstand a direct strike. The odometer showed about 8,000 miles before Tommy reset it to increase its value.

After years of aging in the bike cellar to a fine state of cycling perfection, the sleek red artifact was unearthed, but not for me. I was still too small, and never once would I ride it. Instead I traded it to Tommy for his bike, which was now forty pounds of rust with irresistible features. Tommy sold the prize bike for twenty-five dollars and never looked back. He would not ride a bike again until he was thirty-two years old.

Mom predicted that I would regret the trade and tried to dissuade me from it, but I would have no part of it. She was right, of course. Most of the features on Tommy's bike were no longer operational, and he seemed much happier with his twenty-five dollars than I did with his many-featured relic.

It was a cruel lesson in supply and demand and micro-market forces that I learned that day. Still, I grew to love that old bike in much the same way that couples in arranged marriages eventually resign themselves to one another. And I knew that, despite her well-traveled appearance, she was still a virgin. The odometer told me so.

revenge of the bengal lion

Mom never did like that cat, so when she suggested we dress him up and enter him in the Pet Parade, I was suspicious. I remembered the fate of the duck that gave his life so that I might ride on two wheels. Not a bad trade really, considering that ducks are food, but it wasn't a trade I was eager to execute again. Pets seemed to have a short shelf life around our house. The four chicks that the Easter Bunny brought me lost their fuzz and their cuteness, and to everyone's surprise, turned into chickens. While still in their adolescence, they escaped their pen one day and found refuge on the roof of the house. Leghorns are flyers, we discovered. Mom decided that Easter was long over, and since the chickens didn't have names anyway, they were fair game. She fried them all up in one big iron skillet and served them to us for dinner. I had always been fond of those chickens, and was even more so now that they were on my plate – hot, crispy and dismembered, alongside the mashed potatoes and gravy. When it came to poultry, we were carnivores first and pet-owners second. It was just as well that way. If Mom hadn't gotten to them, the cat would have done the job, but he wouldn't have enjoyed it as much as Mom had.

The cat fell between us and the chickens on the food chain, but he seemed safe from sharing their fate. After all, he was not edible, and he had a name, *Cholla*, which we would have no doubt spelled C-H-O-Y-A had we ever had occasion to write about him. On a camping trip to the desert a few summers before, I had been viciously attacked by a cactus of the same name. It was nicknamed the "jumping cactus" for its propensity to leap out at unsuspecting passersby and sling its spines into their bodies. Dad removed the barbs from my bare legs with pliers, leaving purple blotches behind as vacation souvenirs. That we chose to name our cat after a hostile plant was an omen we should have heeded.

No one remembers where Cholla came from. He may have just shown up on our doorstep one day without first phoning ahead. Kittens are like that. He was the end product of countless generations of indiscriminate breeding. That was common practice for all life forms in Indiana, and everywhere else, too, I discovered later. He was an adorable ball of orange fur – and claws and teeth. Our encounters with him often left us scratched and bleeding. Kittens are like that, we told ourselves.

Cholla was our first and only cat. We were dog people. "Remember Zip?" Dad often asked me, even though Zip had died two years before I was born. Zippy the Wonder Dog, he was, and his legend lives on today. He was the gold standard by which all subsequent pets were measured and found wanting. When Tommy was a toddler, Zip had taught him to run to the door and bark at the sound of the doorbell. Mom and Dad were relieved that in his later years Tommy came to choose his role models more wisely, and except when the moon is full, now answers the door in the stealthy upright fashion preferred by humans.

Zip was the Robert Strom of dogs. Sure, Lassie was smart. She could identify a C-clamp and fetch it on command, but Zip could glue a router-cut sliding dovetail joint and hold it in place to dry with that same C-clamp. She could also bake a heck of a cake, they said, even if she did need a little help with the icing. Cholla had no interest in competing with the Legend of Zip.

Cholla soon grew into a cat, shedding his protective layer of fuzz and kittenish charm and got by on cunning and wile. He never said anything outright, but his contempt for The Legend was evident in his expression. While Cholla adopted a permanent air of disdain, his overtly hostile ways with us subsided. With all of us except with Mom, that is. Each had found a natural adversary in the other, and they were on a collision course with destiny.

One summer day Cholla lay sleeping peacefully on the back step like a furry land mine waiting to be tripped. Loaded up with a basket of wet laundry, Mom stepped out the back door, and long before she got to the clothesline, she hit the minefield. In an instantaneous mindless response to the crushing weight on his tail, Cholla sank his fangs deep into Mom's toe. I sympathized with Mom's pain, but secretly held Cholla blameless. It was justifiable self-defense, and no jury would find otherwise. Mom insisted that Cholla had willingly sacrificed his tail to get a bite out of her, but no one was buying it. But all that was before Frank Buck and the Pet Parade. In hindsight Cholla was only retaliating in advance.

Frank Buck was a great white hunter, a fictional character who lived in the last days of radio on a Saturday morning show called *Bring 'Em Back Alive*. Frank was an environmentalist of sorts, even before the word was known. Each week he penetrated the fiercest jungles on earth and confronted the fiercest beasts in the jungle. Rather than slaughtering them in cold blood, he captured them, often alone and barehanded, and confined them to small cages for the remainder of their natural lives, where they could be observed by thousands of city kids with short attention spans.

I loved Frank Buck. It was only fitting that I would portray him in the Pet Parade, and Cholla would be my savage prize. Mom outfitted Cholla with a dark furry mane, which strikingly offset his natural orange tones, and she carefully painted black accent stripes on his body. He was confined in a cage curiously labeled "Bengal Lion." Mom was in serious danger of having her creative license suspended, but somehow it seemed to work. Cholla skulked in the cage convincingly, playing the part of the unhappy captive. I pulled him down Meridian on my Radio Flyer wagon, while hundreds of kids with short attention spans crowded the parade route. They looked on briefly, then eagerly scanned the street behind me to see what indignities those kids had heaped upon their pets.

Mom's work was successful, as it usually was, but this time the judges awarded us with a meaningless trophy instead of a bike. Apparently, bikes were dispensed only when the pet paid the ultimate price. Mom tried to persuade me that the trophy was a big deal, but I knew that it would never be worth anything, no matter how long it aged in the cellar. As for Cholla, he had the decency not to blow chunks in all directions as the duck had the year before. He also had the wherewithal to survive the parade, but Mom was on his enemies list now for sure, in case there had been any lingering doubts.

After a few years the Pet Parade lost its appeal for the hundreds of short attention span parade-watchers, and that was it. There would be no more Pet Parades or other public assaults on animal dignity.

Summer passed all too soon, as it did every year, and with the first frost Cholla vanished. It would have been easy to suspect that Mom was involved in his disappearance, but we never did. Her recurring refrains of "I wonder what ever happened to that danged cat?" might have been interpreted as transparent attempts to divert our natural suspicions, but it worked well enough to keep Tommy and me from launching an official investigation. We, too, wondered what ever happened to that danged cat.

Our questions were answered in the spring of the next year when Cholla showed up at our doorstep, on Mother's Day no less. If Cholla had anything, it was a magnificent sense of irony. We speculated that he followed the birds south and spent the winter in Miami Beach. He had really let himself go down there. He smelled bad, and his orange fur was a ratty mess. He had gone punk twenty-five years ahead of his time and brought back nothing from Florida but a bad attitude. It was evident he'd been hanging with an unsavory crowd. He dropped all pretenses of feline charm and skulked around the yard in a petulant mood, looking for someone to bite. His opportunity came that very day, when my cousins came up from Indianapolis for the day. Little four-year old Charlotte found herself separated from the safety of the pack, and sought out Cholla to smother with her love. Cholla rewarded her affection with a generous bite into her left hand. Nobody really saw what had happened, but Cholla was presumed guilty and confined without a trial. Mom locked him away in the garage, promising to deny all appeals, not that there would be any.

There could be but one explanation for how a cat from a decent, loving family could go so bad. Rabies! Just as every parent lived in mortal fear of polio in the 1950's, every kid lived in dread of rabies. We knew it could happen, too, because Walt Disney told us so. When Pa raised his gun to put a bullet in Old Yeller, he ripped the heart out of every kid in America, but we understood the alternative. Fourteen shots, one each day, right in the stomach. I imagined that regimen so often it was as if I'd been through it myself. I could feel the needle piercing my stomach, maybe sticking in a ham salad sandwich that I'd had for lunch, but it was that or a hideous, painful death.

According to Mom, there were only two ways to determine whether Cholla had rabies. We could lock him in the garage for two weeks and see if he died, or we could send his severed head to the veterinarian, who would examine his brain for signs of the disease. The vote was close, but confinement won. I wondered whether Charlotte would have been out of luck if we waited two weeks only to find out Cholla was hydrophobic. Would Charlotte begin the four-teen-day regimen of injections or move into her garage for a couple of weeks to see what happened? I kept my fears to myself. Charlotte had enough people worrying for her without my help.

Mom braved attack each day as she entered the garage to feed Cholla. I imagined her slipping the food with a gloved hand through a grate to the increasingly surly Cholla. "Breakfast, Lefty," she would say, then steal away to safety.

Cholla made it through the two weeks, much to the relief of my cousins, but he disappeared again, this time for good. He was gone to Miami Beach, we figured, or some other paradise destination where the behavior of a wayward cat would go unnoticed.

Years later Mom came clean.

"I took him to the animal shelter," she said, "and I told them 'I don't care what you do with this cat. I never want to see it again.'"

I figured the good folks at the animal shelter would overlook Cholla's sociopathic tendencies and put him on the retirement home wing, where he would live out his days eating soft food and watching a TV that was always on a little too loud.

It was a sad but inevitable ending for Cholla, but all things considered, much better than fried cat with mashed potatoes and gravy.

tiny tears, the amazing hydraulic christmas baby

I don't know why I wanted that Tiny Tears doll for Christmas so much. The 1950's were way before Alan Alda and the era of the sensitive male, and that whole "goo-goo, rock and coo" experience that appealed to girls my age turned my stomach.

At the age of seven, guns, swords and other toys of destruction usually topped my list, but I was a sucker for features, and this doll had 'em. Her eyes opened and closed like every other doll, but she was the first to accept a bottle of real liquid and cry real tears and fill her diaper with whatever real stuff went into her mouth.

NOTE: *Tiny Tears, The Incredible Hydraulic Christmas Baby* first appeared in print in *Upon The Midnight Clear: The 2005 Keep It Coming Christmas Anthology*, edited by Guy Adams. Copies are available at www.cafepress.com.

This was a breakthrough trend in which the most undesirable characteristics of real babies were disguised as toys in hopes of eventually reducing the teen pregnancy rate. Regrettably, Tiny Tears did not have that effect, but it did alert an entire generation that whatever goes into a baby eventually comes out the other end.

Tiny Tears was not really my first choice. The big kids in the neighborhood raved about the Slutty Sally doll with its array of terrific features, but I had never seen one. Mom advised me not to ask Santa for it either, because the good and decent elves in Santa's workshop would be producing no such item. Besides, she said, I would want the sort of doll that I could respect, not play with a couple of times behind the garage and cast aside.

My chances of Santa bringing a Tiny Tears doll looked good, I thought. She was affordable without being cheap, posed no choking hazard and wouldn't be provoked to put my eye out. My encounter with Santa took place at Rinker's Hardware store with my friend Mikey. Mikey went first, detailing the cache of weaponry that he expected to see under his tree on Christmas morning. Santa smiled and dumbly nodded his approval, apparently unaware that he had just committed to delivering enough arms to take over Bolivia. When my turn came, I asked for only one thing, the Tiny Tears doll.

Before Santa could respond, Mikey chirped out. "I think he's a sissy, don't you, Santa?"

Without hesitation and in the true spirit of Christmas, Santa came right back at Mikey.

"Yeah," he said.

That pretty much ended our visit. Santa's concurrence did not offend me, but I did wonder who this rummy old man was. Christmas in a hardware store was obviously a gig for Santas on their way out. The other eleven months a year he was probably one of those losers who hung out at the bus station all day, reading the newspaper and feigning interest when the 10:45 from Duluth finally pulled in. I was annoyed at Mikey, though. I had expected better of him, even if he was only five.

Christmas morning came and sure enough Santa did not bring me a doll, Tiny Tears or otherwise. But Mom and Dad did, for their brains had not been rotted by years of living in a frozen wasteland, drinking Sterno out of a paper bag while Mrs. Claus enabled and the codependent elves looked the other way.

The first few days after Christmas I played with Tiny Tears without interruption. I thought of her not so much as a human replica, but as a simulated infantile hydraulic system. Water that went in the top came out the bottom, and water that went in the bottom came out there, too. It was the unadvertised enema feature. What a great toy.

Water soon became a tiresome medium, though, and I experimented with more adventuresome substances. Milk, prune juice and Kool-Aid also went in and out, for the most part, but soon her system became clogged with the undigested remains of a week's play, and she was ripe for a cleaning. Castor oil, I was to find, did not have the same effect on her as it did on me. It only caused her to dribble like an old man with prostate trouble.

By New Year's Day Tiny Tears' constant leaking had become foul and tiresome. We had failed to bond, and I set her aside for good. Meanwhile, Mikey had amassed an impressive arsenal for Christmas, more than one kid could put into action by himself. Seven days of Christmas vacation still lay ahead of us – plenty of time to take over Bolivia and still make it back before school. Tiny Tears would have wanted it that way.

a filling experience

Dr. Boski penciled a few last marks on the tooth chart, then took a long drag on the cigar that had been smoldering in the ashtray during my exam. The blue smoke settled around me like a shroud.

"Looks like ten cavities this time."

"Dngh? Nn-goo?"

Even with two rolls of cotton and the saliva extractor in place, he could understand my every word. He made a quick recount of the blackened teeth on his chart.

"Yep, you do," he said, relieving me of the paraphernalia parked in my mouth. "Six upstairs and four downstairs. Ten altogether."

I was elated. More than half my teeth showed no visible signs of rot. Last year the total had been eighteen cavities, a personal best and a family record that still stands. My wisdom teeth had yet to join the others in my mouth, but I suspected that in a couple of years they would emerge triumphantly as blackened stumps. Dr. Boski conducted nothing more than a holding action against the ongoing decomposition. He was painting the Golden Gate Bridge. No sooner would he finish, than he would begin all over again. He could have sustained his career by giving up his other patients and strip-mining the decay from my teeth alone.

Tooth decay was the legacy of my family, just as hemophilia was for the Romanovs. Nobody could tell us why, and not to point fingers at the Russian royal family, but it was definitely not the result of generations of inbreeding. It was as if our salivary glands dispensed Coca-Cola instead of spit.

Fluoridated water might have helped some, but you wouldn't be finding that in our water supply, by God. It was common knowledge that fluoridating the water supply was right at the top of the Communist agenda. ("If they can put fluoride in your drinking water, who knows what else they can put in it?" I don't know – A slice of lemon perhaps? A paper umbrella?)

Chlorine was okay though. It killed germs and was a freedom-loving, capitalist chemical, unlike the treacherous, pinko fluoride family. To make it worse, you couldn't tell from the periodic table of elements which chemicals were aligned with the Red Menace. There chlorine and fluorine were, in the same electron group, one good twin, one evil, indistinguishable to all but the self-appointed guardians of freedom who protected our water supply and our minds with equal zeal.

Fluorine and its fellow travelers blended in with the others, biding their time. I'm certain that some had found their way into our mouths. They may have even sneaked in with the toothpaste. I considered not brushing for six months to see whether that would improve my dental health, but I collapsed under the parental pressure.

Dr. Boski leafed though his weathered appointment book, dropping ashes on each page. Monday and Tuesday were out. Ash Wednesday, too.

He scribbled out a card for me listing appointments for Thursday, Friday and Saturday. If only his appointment reminders were baseball cards. I would have had every player in the National League. Twice.

Thursday

"Roosevelt killed himself you know," Dr. Boski asserted.

"Huh?" His remark caught me by surprise. I was naively expecting a conversation about my teeth.

"Yep. He's out in the park in his wheelchair, and he tells his attendant to leave him alone for a minute so he can take a whiz. Then Roosevelt wheels himself behind a bush and shoots himself. "

"I never knew that," I said, not that I ever knew about stuff like that.

"Well, of course you wouldn't. They've covered it up!"

I felt privileged to be the keeper of such an important fact while those around me remained blissfully ignorant. I wanted to tell everyone of Dr. Boski's secret, but I decided to hold onto it until I became a contestant on *The $64,000 Question*.

"The last president to die in office was Franklin Roosevelt in 1945. For $64,000 what was the cause of his death? "

Triumphantly, I would reveal to the world that FDR had died while taking a whiz in the park. America would surely forget about that punk Robert Strom after a coup like that.

In a blatant attempt to redirect his attention from my teeth I asked follow-up questions until he was exhausted. What about the attendant? Didn't they suspect him? How do you take a whiz from a wheelchair? Do you think Roosevelt would still be president today if he hadn't died? Dr. Boski didn't like that idea very much, but the truth was that if FDR's name had been on the ballot, he would have carried thirty-five states, even if he had been dead for fifteen years.

I was none too eager to undergo Dr. Boski's medieval process of tooth repair, but the FDR ploy was going to get me only so far. Dr. Boski didn't believe in the use of anesthetics, except for extractions, and this day was set aside for major drilling and excavation.

He peered into my mouth at the many targets of opportunity and fired up his low speed drill. I winced as he whittled away at an offending molar, and soon I was squirming in the chair. I shut my eyes and imagined Dr. Boski wearing a black leather mask, while my tooth chips flew. When my cries of agony finally became too much for Dr. Boski to bear, he put down the drill and fired an icy blast of non-fluoridated mint-flavored water into the cavity. It was a dance we both knew by the numbers. Drill, squirm, scream. Drill, squirm, scream. Rinse and repeat.

"We're getting pretty close to the nerve," he observed from my shrieks. "I'll put something in there to desensitize it and finish you off next time."

Friday

Dr. Boski had no hygienist, no receptionist, no help of any kind. His was a very informal one-man operation. On the occasions when I knew there would be no pain coming my way, I'd walk into his office and chat with him while he worked on other patients. On this afternoon though, I practiced a strategy of avoidance, sitting quietly in his waiting room. There was little of interest for me there, just a stack of *Highlights for Children* magazines and another of *National Geographics*. I had long found *Highlights* to be tedious and derivative. ("How many words can you make using only the letters found in CAT?") My visits were so frequent that I had read the set of *National Geographics* exhaustively. I was well aware, for example, that prospectors in 1933 had happened upon a million Stone Age natives in New Guinea, though presumably not all at once, who were previously unknown to the outside world. I would work this tidbit into conversations for years to come, and, not surprisingly, it would make me a much sought-after dinner guest. Mostly though, I just sat in the least conspicuous corner of Dr. Boski's eight by eight waiting room, mentally rehearsing the torture that was to come.

One by one, my fellow patients waiting with me took their turns in the chair, each entering Boski's inner sanctum without waiting for a summons. I sat quietly, daring not to move or scratch lest Dr. Boski hear me. I entertained myself by listening for cries for mercy from those patients who had preceded me, but they never cracked. Dr. Boski's patients were made of pretty tough stuff, and one day I would be too.

After the last patient walked out, five minutes passed, then ten, then fifteen. Then the office went dark and Dr. Boski stepped into the waiting room, cigar in mouth. I nonchalantly pretended to read again about the Stone Age natives of New Guinea.

"Oh!" he said. "I didn't know you were here!"

I had been there for an hour and fifteen minutes, but it didn't matter now. His office was closed. The drill was still smoking but down for the night. His black leather mask was neatly tucked away with his spiked collar. I had prevailed in our little game of cat and mouse, and we both knew it.

Saturday

Hiding out would be futile on this morning. The same trick wasn't going to work for me two days in a row. Besides, I was his first appointment, arriving even before his first cigar. Reluctantly, I turned myself in, and after the usual round of pleasantries Dr. Boski clipped a napkin around my neck. Unnatural as it may have seemed, I had a genuine affection for Dr. Boski. Stockholm syndrome? I don't think so. If it were not for the regimen of pain he had reserved for me, I probably would have dropped in to see him every day on the way home from school. That was not the case, however. If I were in no pain, he could be counted on to inflict a healthy dose of it, but if I were already hurting, he always had a way to make me feel better. Once he even met me in his office after church on Palm Sunday to treat an abscessed tooth that had been the source of a long tearful night. For that alone he won my undying gratitude.

On this particular day Dr. Boski bypassed all political commentary and went straight to work, prying the temporary filling from my molar, cavity number one of ten. Just as he had promised, there was far less pain – and less squirming, wincing and screaming – than on my initial visit. He sized up the gaping cavity and with quick precision prepared a generous dollop of cement. Carefully, he packed it into place and instructed me to keep my mouth open a couple of minutes while it set. I fantasized about carving my initials in the wet cement, but could say no more than "Argh ngh-nngh ookh!" which went uninterpreted.

Without a word Dr. Boski turned his attention to the acne sprouting profusely across my face and squeezed a couple of the more inviting targets with the same tweezers that only moments before had held a ball of cotton. Who could resist a ripe pimple? Not me, and apparently not Dr. Boski either.

"Bad Blood!" he declared. "That's where these come from!"

Bad Blood? Oh no, I thought, please don't get out the leeches! But fortune smiled upon me, for either Dr. Boski had no leeches or they'd already had breakfast. Bad Blood was a Communist invention, plain and simple, and the Commies certainly knew how to exploit it to destroy our faces. And if our faces succumbed so easily, then our minds would not be far behind, until soon all of America was watching inane television shows and listening to rock and roll music, and we had all lost the will to resist. There was no need to state the obvious. We both knew it was true. I considered the pimplish debris left behind on his tweezers and offered up a prayer of gratitude for being the first kid in his chair that day.

"Okay," he said. "Let's take a look at that filling, so we can get you on your way."

He examined his work long and hard, expanding his area of interest to the neighboring teeth, using all the lights, mirrors and magnifiers at his disposal. He furrowed his brows, shook his head and muttered sounds that were not reassuring, sounds that announced "More Pain Ahead."

Dr. Boski pored over my tooth chart, marking his first victory in this current campaign, but he also added fresh new spots of black to offset his progress.

"Two new cavities," he said, lighting his first cigar of the day.

"What are you doing after school next week?" he asked, dropping ashes onto his open appointment book

"Me?" I shrugged. "The usual, I guess."

strikes and birdies

With its gentle rolling hills, grassy expanses and old-growth maple trees, the Maplewood Cemetery could have been the back nine of the golf course at The Club. Like The Club, the cemetery offered a serene and tranquil environment for those aboveground from spring through autumn. The similarities ended there though, for the cemetery was far less exclusive with its membership requirements. All you needed was a note from your doctor certifying that your autopsy came back positive, and you were in. Welcome to the other club, Club Dead. No annual fees. No ups. No extras.

Membership at The Club marked the social classes as clearly as did life and death. The social strata could be delineated into golfers and bowlers. Golf was the domain of the wealthy, while bowling was the sport of the blue-collar elite. Dad was a mail carrier, so naturally, we were bowlers, and we wore our humility with arrogant pride.

My best friend Jimmy was a golfer, the natural domain of a physician's son, and he wore his arrogance with proud humility. Golf represented all that was unattainable to us –

crustless sandwiches with watercress, high-octane gas, taxicabs and airplanes, and after-eight dinners at The Club in the company of people with winter tans. Jimmy and I spent countless hours proselytizing for the games to which we were born, even dabbling in one another's sports. Jimmy became a passable bowler, though never acquiring the blue-collar grace inherent in my style. I became a skilled miniature golfer, not that it counted for anything. "Real" golf was spending spring break at Ipanema Beach amid the floss goddesses. Miniature golf was watching *Lifestyles of the Rich and Famous* while eating Cheetos out of the box, then wiping your hands on your jeans.

"Come with me Saturday," Jimmy said one day. "I'm playing a round with Lester, this kid from The Club. See what it's like to commune with God for eighteen holes."

It was one of those rare Saturday mornings where I was not communing with the dentist, so I accepted, knowing that even if the game was a drag, I could at least look forward to a free lunch of crustless sandwiches and umbrella drinks. At the appointed hour Jimmy arrived, stylishly costumed in a Ban-Lon shirt and loose checkered pants. Ever the height of fashion, I also wore a Ban-Lon shirt, but with long stiff Bermuda shorts and matching powder blue knee socks. Mom had seen the look in the Sears catalog, the Official guide to fashion in Central Indiana, and had fallen in love with it on my behalf. I think she even used the word "cute." Oh, how I longed for a loose-fitting five button shirt in bold primary colors that said "Louie's Heating and Cooling" or "White River Dump & Refuse" on the back with my name stitched across the front pocket in a nice loopy cursive. Over my fierce objections Mom saw to it that I was properly attired for my maiden voyage at The Club.

"You'll be fine," she assured me. "I talked to Jimmy's mother, and this is what they're wearing now."

Who "they" were was a constant source of mystery to me, a mystery like the Virgin Birth or seedless watermelons, where the laws of reproduction are temporarily suspended for a good cause. Is it going to rain tomorrow? That's what "they" say. Should I stick with non-detergent oil for my car? That's what "they" say. Should I dress like a geek for my day at The Club? Apparently, that's what "they" said. I somehow suspected that when I got to The Club, "they" wouldn't be there.

I was right. We got to the club and "they" weren't there. Jimmy's friend Lester was there though, and he wasn't dressed like either one of us. Apparently, he hadn't bothered to confer with Jimmy's mom or mine, because he was dressed in clothes that could be safely worn on the street. Jimmy slipped out of his Hush Puppies and completed his transformation with a pair of cleated black and white saddle shoes. He wore his wardrobe quite unself-consciously, a tendency that would not serve him particularly well in our college years.

Jimmy did not bother to introduce me to Lester, but I knew who he was, and I assumed he knew of me. Lester didn't say much, but when he did it was with a considerable stutter. "Y-Y-Y-Your t-t-t-turn, J-J-J-Jimmy!"

Jimmy extracted a small wooden object from thin air, stuck it into the ground and set his ball on top of it. So this was a golf tee! Only weeks before our science teacher had shown us an engine valve from a car, and asked if we knew what it was. I was the first to answer, confident that my enthusiasm and expertise would carry the day.

"It's a golf tee!" I cried out. It was the same shape as all the tees I'd ever seen in cartoons, but I was the archetypal bowler and completely unaware that tees were not a half a foot long and made of forged steel. I may as well have identified it as a side-gilled sea slug.

"A golf tee?" he shouted back. "He says it's a golf tee!"

It was clear from his incredulous – no contemptuous! – tone that he'd never met one so naïve about a game he held dear. (He was one of "them!") He would forever know me, I was certain, as that idiot savant in his class who did not know a golf tee from an engine valve.

From his bag Jimmy took a brand new Titleist and set it carefully on the tee. He took several swings, missing each time. These he characterized as "practice swings" and informed me that they would not count in his score. This bizarre custom merely strengthened my belief that bowling was an ethically superior sport. No self-respecting bowler would dare make the case that gutter balls were practice balls. Nevertheless, Jimmy and Lester continued in this manner, unapologetically taking practice swings with impunity. In overt disregard for all sense of fair play they had entered into a conspiracy of two to disregard such strokes, no matter how blatant.

On the fourth hole Jimmy's shot to the green left him within a few inches of the hole. Rather than tapping it in, he pocketed the ball, describing it as a "gimme." This action he took with no apparent shame. It was as if he had left the seven pin standing after his first ball, hit the reset button and given himself a spare. A strange game was playing itself out here at The Club, a place awash in natural beauty but ultimately a desolate moral landscape.

On the eleventh hole Lester shanked his drive into the woods. With a resounding "Goddammit!" he pitched his driver toward where the ball had last been seen. And no sooner had Lester spoken God's name, than did His hand reach down from the heavens and touch Lester's mouth, for the *Goddammit!* rang out in perfect clarity with nary a trace of a stutter. It was a capricious God that day though, for no matter what else Lester spoke, each word was an alliteration unto itself. It was "N-n-n-ice sh-sh-shot, J-J-Jimmy" here and "P-p-p-playing th-th-through" there. There were more *Goddammit*s though, and each subsequent vain usage of the Lord's name was a perfect articulate replica of the first. If Lester were to covet his neighbor's wife aloud or verbally dishonor his father and mother, I wondered, would his speech be equally pristine? The results of such an experiment, if one did take place, would be unknown to me, for Lester disappeared into the clubhouse after he putted out on eighteen, and I would never see him again.

"So, what was your score, Jimmy? I never saw you guys write anything down."

"My score? Let's see, I shot forty-one on the front nine, bogeyed ten, parred eleven, three-putted twelve ..."

He looked to the sky for answers and tabulated them on his fingers as they came in.

"Eighty-four!" he said. "Not bad, huh?"

"Are you telling me that you remember your score from every hole?"

"Yeah. What about it?"

"No way could I bowl ten frames and score 'em from memory. How could you just total up eighteen holes in your head?"

He shrugged me off. "I've played this game before."

"I bet you have," I muttered, but not loud enough to jeopardize my shot at a crust-free sandwich.

"C'mon," he said. "Let's eat."

The Club Grille was my first foray into the sumptuous repast from the other side of the tracks, and I wanted to milk it for its full value. I scanned the menu eagerly, but found no *Ben Hoagies* or *Jack Pumpernicklaus*. Watercress was as scarce as bread crust was plentiful. The Club cuisine was the same as the proles got on the outside – the same as the bowling alley! Oh, sure, they had a special Club Shrimp Cocktail, but that choice was out. I figured it to be a drink, and we Methodists never touched the stuff. We settled on burgers and Cokes. As always, fries were involved. Nearby somebody lit a cigarette, and it was easy to close my eyes and imagine that I was at the bowling alley.

"So, what is it about this game," I asked after the last French fry was safely in my mouth, "that makes you think it's better than bowling?"

Jimmy muttered a lot of stuff about difficulty and tradition and playing in the great outdoors. Then he came clean.

"You want to know the truth, Bob?" He stared off into the hazy blue sky, where the truth lay hidden with his scores. "I really just come here for the food."

gaseous maximus

The average person passes about a liter of gas per day, spread out over an average of fourteen separate outbursts. Five thousand times a year the natural processes of our bodies are pitted against the rules imposed by polite society. The prohibitions are so unforgiving that even the sound is considered offensive, and we are left seeking moments alone where we may obey our bodies lest we explode and burst into flames.

I lost the gas battle in spectacular fashion in front of Karen Kupchek on April 12, 1962. In a lifetime of gas-passing, that is the one that I would most like to rescind.

Karen was a goddess with a radiant smile and a body made fit and golden brown by endless hours of tennis in the summer sun. Unfortunately, I could worship at her altar only within the sweaty confines of my fourteen-year old mind. Physical or even social contact was out of the question. I was a geek, and a goddess does, after all, have her standards. We sat back to back at tables in biology class, and I constantly manufactured opportunities to turn around and gaze upon her magnificence – a dropped pencil here, a look out the window there, a conversation with the nameless person beside her. It was all part of my daily regimen. On one such occasion I dropped a sheet of paper, and when I bent down to retrieve it, a mighty roar emanated from behind me. The fart that roared had been laying in wait by the exit, gathering its strength like a hurricane and selecting the optimal moment to betray me. As farts go, this one was breathtaking, perfectly formed and unmistakable. No one would mistake this baby for the sound of a chair dragging or a cheap imitation from an adolescent armpit or mouth. Nope, this was the real thing.

Karen never looked around, never mentioned it, and never brought it up at our class reunion twenty years later, but I'm sure it was her most memorable fart, too, because she most certainly never passed gas. I'm also quite certain that she visited the bathroom only as a social obligation and not to fulfill any tawdry biological necessities. My story has no doubt been recounted many times throughout her years.

"Sure, I remember the time Bob Deaton farted in biology class. I remember it like the day Elvis was drafted. Mr. Heinz was droning on about the symbiotic relationship between the Philippine hermit crab and the sea anemone when it came. I swear Bob's guts must have exploded. I didn't dare move afterwards. I just sat perfectly still, and didn't breathe for about eight minutes. Three people around me passed out and one of them was hospitalized. I think maybe he died. When I couldn't hold my breath any longer, I opened the jar of pickled salamanders and used the formaldehyde as an air freshener. What ever happened to Bob? I don't know, but I'm pretty sure he got an *A* in that class. I still have one of those salamanders somewhere."

In my perfect world passing gas is not a source of shame, but a respected sport like ice dancing or demolition derby. The occasional outburst in biology class would merely be conscientious training. And Karen Kupchek would worship me.

It all started at the Madison County Fair in 1967 where I took home a blue ribbon at the annual Windbreakers Meet. It was the year before Competitive Flatulence went international with the Sydney Gas Games. Contestants were judged on the timbre, duration, creativity and, of course, aroma of their efforts. Like other top competitors, I followed a strict training regimen of whole grains for volume and for fragrance, lightly spiced cabbage. With the dedication of a scholar I scrutinized newsletters devoted to the sport as if they were holy texts: *Training for Flavor – Red Cabbage or Green?*, *The Perfect Fart – Will We See It in Our Lifetimes?* and *Ed Beeley breaks duration record with 90-second effort!* I was prepared in every way. I was at the top of my game.

Going into the final round the defending champion was leading in points, but I had yet to perform my routine. From the moment I stepped up to the platform and dropped my pants, the crowd knew that they were in for something special. My silk boxers glistened in the afternoon sunlight and stood in marked contrast to the more conventional cotton briefs favored by my competitors. The audience gasped in a single voice. I began my performance with a subtle prelude of flatulent trills, teased the crowd with a trip up the chromatic scale, changing scents twice along the way, and finished off with a four bar clip from *Fur Elise*. It was a transcendent experience for those present that day, and it raised the bar for the whole sport of competitive flatulence. The next year at Sydney I claimed top honors with a rendition of *Flight of the Bumblebee*. Four years later at the World Cup in Lima I led a team to a gold medal with a presentation of Franz Liszt's *Hungarian Dance # 2* in four parts plus percussion.

At our twentieth class reunion, Karen sought me out, gathered our classmates in a reverent circle around me and implored me for a reprise. But, regretfully, I declined. An artiste does, after all, have his standards.

health and salvation

Jeanette Franklin, who was of no particular interest to me, sat behind me in Mrs. Yardow's eighth grade health class. One day she struck me hard on the head with her spelling book, either because she liked me or because she didn't. What memories she permanently dislodged I don't know, but sex education was not among them. The Indiana Board of Education had decided that our education in that subject was best served through independent studies. Some of the more ambitious students had been pursuing that course since seventh grade, and the occasional pregnant fourteen-year old attested to their diligence with the lab work, even if they showed little mastery of the course material.

The same week as the Jeanette Franklin attack, we heard live coverage of Alan Shepherd becoming the first American in space. It was a day of excitement and pride for all of us. It was also another day of apprehension for me, because I never knew when Jeanette Franklin would unleash another one, this time with heavier artillery, like a U.S. history book.

The life-changing event that year was Mrs. Yardow's big poster contest. As she did every year, she gave out the assignment of making a poster that warned of the perils of drinking or smoking. All our posters would be entered into the contest, and some lucky winner would receive a cash prize of fifteen dollars. As inspiration the entire eighth grade had been treated to a graphic film of a surgery in which a cancerous lung was removed. The slimy blackened mass we would see in the surgeon's hands, we were told, was the result of a lifetime of tireless smoking. The day of the screening, the tension built from one class to the next, and stories circulated of girls fainting and boys crying like babies. Surprisingly, every kid in my class held on to both his dignity and his lunch, and we all pledged never to smoke in this life or the next.

Satisfied that smoking was pretty well covered, I decided that this was the year to specialize in alcohol. Most entries were crude affairs with crayon-drawn letters that proclaimed "Alcohol is Dangerous. So is Smoking" or the more esoteric "If you drink, don't smoke." Inevitably there would be a pen and ink drawing of a dead guy. Not mine. My poster was professional quality with a zippy slogan, "Seeing Double Is Not the Same as Looking Twice." It was accompanied by a double exposure of somebody – I think it was me – at the wheel of a car with a bottle in hand.

Normally, I would have drawn a picture of a dead guy with a ballpoint pen and topped it off with a punchy maxim like "Drinking is Bad. Real Bad," but Mom and my brother Tom intervened to save me from drowning in the bathwater of my own artistic mediocrity. Tom handled the trick photography, and Mom did the rest. Each step of the way Mom would say "Okay, now you're going to want to do this." Then she did it. My job was to hand her the scissors and paste. It was our way of fooling ourselves into believing that it was my project and that she was merely providing appropriate parental guidance. Dad also provided appropriate parental guidance. He went to bed and left me to do my project myself.

The poster was a masterpiece, and under Mom's watchful eye I carefully signed my name. She was clearly proud of the end results, my so-so signature notwithstanding. The other crayon and ink entries were no match, and the first place award of fifteen dollars went to me, Bob Deaton. All the recognition and prize money helped to persuade me that the project had been mine all along. I imagined that the sociological impact of "my" poster would be immeasurable. Eighth-graders throughout the school would be inspired to confine their drinking to home for the rest of the school year and pledge to drive only during daylight hours. I was a hero. It felt good to make a difference – and to collect fifteen bucks.

Not long after I had captured top honors in the poster contest, I was notified by the Women's Christian Temperance Union that I had won a free week at summer camp, Camp Temperance-By-The-Lake. Whether they had sponsored the poster contest, I don't know. They may have simply been looking for an anti-alcohol crusader with good graphical presentation skills.

The brochure depicted Camp Temperance-By-The-Lake as an Eden without the serpent, nestled into the wooded hills of southern Indiana and staffed by caring camp counselors dedicated to making my camp experience a memorable one.

"If you play a musical instrument, be sure to bring it," the brochure urged. My mastery of the trombone was on par with my poster making skills. That is, I was average at best, but with the right Tommy Dorsey record on the phonograph, I could perform a convincing slide-synch to *Getting Sentimental Over You*. There was no room for Tommy Dorsey in my luggage, but the trombone was required and went with me, no questions asked.

I had never been away from home alone before, and even though I knew not one other person at Camp Temperance-By-The-Lake, I was confident that I would adapt nicely and that my camp experience would be memorable. I was partly right.

I rode down on a Sunday with some local folks. The driver was a woman of undue cheerfulness, somebody's mom I think. One of the older kids in the car, a goofy guy named Albert, wanted to be a U.S. Senator and professed his lust for a girl named Patty, who would be at camp. Two days later Albert and I would see a kid with no prospects offer Patty fifty cents for a kiss, and she would decline.

The camp looked like the brochure, which depicted an inviting pool of sorts outside the two residence halls. The pool was affectionately referred to as The Deep Freeze. I soon learned that it was the last vestige of the Ice Age in Indiana, explaining the dearth of swimmers in the brochure. No lifeguards were needed, and none would have entered the water even if they had been. Shortly after I settled in to my bunk in the boys' residence hall, I discovered that no one else had heeded the plea in the brochure to bring a musical instrument. I hid my trombone under my bunk and hoped it would not be discovered.

This was my first experience at summer camp, and I never gave much thought to the WCTU angle. A camp where there was no alcohol? So what? Wasn't YMCA camp like that? Camp Temperance-By-The-Lake had the usual build-a-birdhouse-out-of-Popsicle-sticks and make-a-lanyard-for-Mom activities, but most of our time was consumed by Reverend Elwood and his two-a-day prayer meetings and endless classes after breakfast on what the Bible really meant. The good folks back at First Methodist never told me, for example, that all references to wine in the Bible were to be interpreted as fruit juice. Revered Elwood offered no real explanation for this remarkable suspension of fermentation, other than 'Jesus was not the kind of guy who would drink.' It was a divinely inspired triumph of belief over chemistry. I, for one, was convinced.

As the days dragged on, I made no real connection with the other kids – although I did briefly consider offering Patty fifty cents if she'd be my friend for fifteen minutes – and I was overtaken by homesickness. Thursday was Visitors' Day when official contact with the outside world was sanctioned, and Mom drove down to see me. Camp was over in two more days, but I pleaded with Mom to take me home immediately. She gently declined, reminding me that there were still lanyards to tie and birdhouses to finish and lessons in the alchemy of wine to look forward to. I would have done the same thing if I had been her, but neither of us knew what was coming next.

I was a virtual captive, away from family and friends and subjected to relentless indoctrination. I was prepared to join Patty Hearst and the Symbionese Liberation Army, had they existed then, or the Fear of God Congregational Church just to escape the growing dread accumulating in the corners of my mind.

Thursday night was the bonfire and the climactic spiritual event of the week. Each of us was given a small roll of paper, on which we were to summarize our relationship with God. One by one we would toss the papers into the fire with a verbal proclamation that would please both God and the camp clergy. The legend was that somebody in years past had not been saved and his paper refused to burn, even though it lay in the fiercest flames. His paper didn't burn, but he did, and for a very long time, they said. The idea that my paper might not burn terrified me. I didn't know whether I was saved or even what "saved" meant. If I could have, I would have secretly soaked my paper in gasoline to improve my chances, but all the flammable liquids in camp had been inexplicably transformed to fruit juice.

It was implicit that our proclamations would be delivered in sixteenth-century English, so God could better comprehend them. Patty took a step toward the fire and kicked off the ritual.

"I thank thee O Lord for thy bountiful, uh, bounty."

Nervously, she tossed her paper roll into the fire, and it was instantly consumed by flames. I would have paid her fifty cents for her proclamation, maybe a buck. A lot was riding on this. Patty was still sighing her relief when Albert stepped forward with his proclamation.

"I thank thee Lord for thy bountiful bounty," he said weakly.

"That one's been used, Albert," Reverend Elwood said. "Try another one."

It was clear that Senator Albert had no backup plan.

"Yea though I walk through the valley of bounty, Thou art bountiful."

He quickly tossed his paper into the flames before he could get a negative review from Reverend Elwood and seconds later it was ash. Clearly, it didn't much matter what you said, as long as you were saved.

Two or three others threw in their papers, sticking with variations on the bounty theme, and were pleased to see them consumed in one small fiery miracle after another.

My turn came around all too soon. On my paper I had scrawled "I Believe." I had intended to write a more comprehensive Statement of Beliefs, but time ran out. I prayed that they were wrong about the road to Hell being paved with good intentions.

The bounty theme was working well, so I decided to ride the streak. A look of growing disapproval crossed Reverend Elwood's face with each succeeding *bounty*, but the paper rolls all burst into flames before he could get a "Thou shalt not" out of his mouth, and that's what counted. When my turn began, he issued a stern warning.

"No more bounties!"

Like Albert I had no Plan B, but I quickly pieced together random phrases into something I hoped would sound suitably religious.

"O Lord, Thy will be my tendon juice!"

I didn't know what it meant, but I thought I had a shot as long as it began with "O Lord" and contained at least one sixteenth-century pronoun. I pitched my paper roll into the fire, missing my mark by a few inches. The paper lay there, cold and intact, and a fearful silence gripped everyone in the circle. All eyes were on me, waiting to see the immortal soul sucked from my body, but the paper caught fire, slowly at first, and it was eventually consumed. I had narrowly escaped with a warning shot from God.

In rapid succession the remaining campers in the circle tossed in their papers and made proclamations sufficient to ensure combustion. Relief replaced panic, and we adjourned to the chapel for Part Two.

The chapel was warm and stuffy, like it was every evening. Some combination of heat and the fear of God left all of us glowing with sweat. I was still sorting out the events that had just taken place around the bonfire and was paying little attention when the service began. Nothing out of the ordinary seemed to be going on, but the air was electric. I heard Reverend Elwood invoke the names of the usual biblical cast of characters, running on in his fine midwestern rendition of Middle English. He said something about *lambs* and *hosts* and *Holy Spirit* and used a cadence and terminology that was unlike anything I'd ever heard at our church back home.

Then without warning he shouted, "BE YE SAVED?"

He pointed his finger at us in a slow arc and repeated, "CHILDREN, BE YE SAVED FROM SATAN?"

That was a cue that meant something to kids all around me, and without warning many burst into tears, some of them sobbing uncontrollably. I had fallen through the looking glass into an unfamiliar land. This was a play where everyone else knew his part, and I had wandered onto the stage by accident. I watched in fear as Reverend Elwood and the other camp ministers prayed with my fellow campers, each one alone and shuddering in the night.

How long all this went on, I can't say, but I was greatly relieved when I was able to escape. Still, a profound uneasiness hung over me. I didn't know what it meant to be saved, but the process looked painful. I hadn't melted down like many of my fellow campers had, but maybe I had been coincidentally saved by my proximity to them. Before I went to bed, I shared my concerns with Albert. He himself had been saved just an hour before, and I was hoping that he could give me some answers while it was still fresh in his mind.

"It's real simple, Bob. Just pray to accept Jesus into your life as your personal savior."

"That's it?"

"That's it. It's kind of like drawing a Get-out-of-Hell free card that's good for life."

I prayed pray fervently as Albert instructed, taking special care not to add my customary appeal to wake up dry – and not in the temperance sense.

After a few minutes of serious petitioning to the Almighty I announced to Albert that I was now saved, too, and he welcomed me to the club. Still, I didn't feel any different, so I did it one more time, again with no apparent effect. Maybe I was already saved, and like an extra vaccination, it added no value. It was a question I would leave for another day. I fell asleep knowing that in the morning I would be eight hours closer to going home, and that's all that mattered.

I awoke Friday to a beautiful sunny day and immediately began the countdown to my re-entry into normalcy. While still in my bunk I rattled off the prayer of salvation one more time, in case it had worn off during the night. The results were the same as they had been eight hours earlier. Once again I failed to decompose into a sobbing mess as many of my fellow campers had. For a moment I caught a whiff of what seemed to be the sulfurous fumes of Hell, but it was only the French toast burning in the mess hall.

Before I reached the source of the fumes I was intercepted by Dave, the camp counselor, who had found out about the trombone hiding under my bed. I could see what was coming. *No alcohol, tobacco or trombones allowed in camp, son. We're going to have to place you under arrest.*

"We'd like you to play tonight at the awards ceremony," he said.

"Play what?" It was all over now. He'd want the *Minute Waltz in forty-five seconds*, and if it weren't flawless, I'd be sentenced to stay at camp until it was.

"Just some fanfares when we pass out the awards. Grab your horn and meet me here after this morning's service."

Then he disappeared before I could decline.

To my relief, the morning service was a low-key event. No additional souls were saved, and none were lost. I prayed long and hard, not for salvation, but for relief from my fanfare gig. I wasn't that good to begin with – my trombone teacher was fond of describing my technique as "like a pig farting bran in a barrel" – and a week without practice would doubtless take me to new depths of musicianship. Divine intervention was called for.

Unfortunately, Dave intervened before God could get there, and for the next hour we worked out fanfares appropriate for each award. The citation for best lanyard was a simple three-note piece, but they grew in complexity with the significance of the achievement. The ultimate honor was King and Queen of Temperance, and the fanfare Dave had devised taxed both my endurance and my range. If I hadn't felt the Fear of God the night before, I surely would this night.

I was thankful that I was less than a day away from my parole, and the dread of the evening ceremony had actually made time pass more quickly. I sat alone with my horn in a remote corner of the mess hall as my fellow campers filed in. One veteran of many summers at Camp Temperance-By-The-Lake stopped to offer his condolences.

"First year, huh, kid?"

"Yeah, how'd you know?"

He snorted and tapped my trombone with his finger.

"You'll learn," he said. "You'll learn."

All too soon the awards began, and I rattled off one fanfare after another, missing few notes along the way, but sounding not unlike a pig with gas pains.

"And now," Dave announced, "the award for King and Queen of Temperance goes to the boy and girl who best exemplify the values of Godliness, virtue, abstinence, and, of course, temperance. The fanfare, please."

I raised the trombone to my lips and issued a honk and a blat before I recovered and pushed on stolidly to the end. The fanfare climaxed with a high B flat, a note I could hit only if the planetary alignment was favorable. I had reached it earlier that day, but now the planets conspired against me. Like Sisyphus pushing the stone up the hill, I vainly scratched at the high B flat over and over, sliding down to the A flat below each time.

In morbid fascination Dave watched me twist in the wind before finally crying out in mercy, "Albert Reed and Patty Daly!"

Albert looked mightily pleased with himself, especially sharing the honor with Patty, and thanked me heartily for my fanfare. He went on a bit about his commitment to rule wisely over the kingdom of the temperate. By this point in the program the campers had become restless and didn't care much about who were the King and Queen of Temperance, especially since temperance was a solitary pursuit that didn't ordinarily involve royalty. Patty merely said a gracious *thank you* and posed with Albert for a picture in their ridiculous crowns. I fully expected to see that photo on a campaign poster in twenty years when Albert ran for Senate.

"Before you all go," Dave announced, "we have one more award, this one for Outstanding Camper."

I hurriedly scrambled through my program notes looking for the Outstanding Camper fanfare, but came up empty, not that it mattered. I had blown myself out in search of the elusive high B flat moments before.

"Bob Deaton!" he called.

Oh, no! Not only did Dave want a fanfare, he was calling out my name to make sure that everyone remembered the fat kid with the trombone who refused to play in honor of the

Outstanding Camper. I raised my horn, hoping there was something left in there, when he cried out again.

"Bob Deaton, Outstanding Camper!"

I struggled to imagine some context where "Bob Deaton" and "Outstanding Camper" belonged in the same breath. I had done nothing all week but count the hours until I could leave. At craft time I had scarcely fashioned the beginnings of a birdhouse ghetto. The lanyard eluded me completely. With limited space in my head for that sort of thing, I knew that mastering that craft meant I would never tie my shoes again. My paper roll had barely ignited. And I missed the high B flat.

"The award goes to Bob Deaton for bringing his horn to camp and for, uh, being outstanding."

Without comment and in complete disbelief I accepted the certificate to scattered, bored applause. Some of the older campers were already making their way to the doors. If Dave had handed me the head of the Loch Ness monster, I could not have been more surprised. Before I went to bed I tucked the certificate into my suitcase and never saw it again.

Early Saturday morning we were subjected to one final gathering before our parole into the Real World. Reverend Elwood offered up a prayer of gratitude for those that were saved, that they should know the Lord better. He prayed especially long and hard for those unsaved pretenders among us, because God does not look kindly upon the unrepentant sinner. At the conclusion of the service we were asked to sign our release papers, a pledge stating that we would never, ever under any circumstances accept drink or smoke, no matter how graciously it was offered for the rest of our earthly existence, so help us God. Everyone signed with good intentions, though most were in too much of a hurry to read the fine print that detailed what awaited backsliders in this life and the next.

The cheerful lady who delivered us the week before was there to retrieve us right at the appointed hour. Her car had barely stopped rolling when I jammed my gear into her trunk and jumped into the back seat, a strategy that earned me the middle spot over the hump. Albert sat to my right and wore his crown all the way home. I was sure that he would sleep in it that night, as he had the night before.

The dubious status of my salvation continued to eat at me, and I appealed my case to Albert, figuring that the King of Temperance had improved his status with the Almighty.

"Albert," I said, "how do I know if I'm saved? I prayed like you told me, but I don't feel any different."

"Bob, let me put it like this," Albert said, holding up fingers crossed in make-a-wish fashion. "Reverend Elwood and the Lord are just like this."

"Yeah," I said. "I think I read that in the brochure. What's that got to do with me?"

"You think they're going to give the Outstanding Camper award to somebody who's not saved? You're in, Buddy! You're in!"

The King of Temperance had spoken, and that was good enough for me.

My homecoming was a joyous occasion. I was the confederate soldier at war's end limping up the country road to the old homestead. The whole family gathered on the front porch, Mom with an apple pie in her hands. Tears glistened in everyone's eyes.

"Ma, Pa," I say. " I'm home from the war."

"We missed ye, Sonny," Ma says. "Have some pie."

Over pie I relived my first person account of Thursday night's terror. When I finished, Mom refreshed my milk and cut me another generous slice. Her words filled me with a profound sense of comfort and peace, feelings that had eluded me in my brush with salvation two days before.

"We're Methodists, Bobby," she said. "We don't need to be saved."

forty-three to one

In the 1960's Pope John XXIII gave his best shot at gathering the faithful of the world under one big umbrella. Unification, they called it, but the faithful were content under their own little umbrellas, and his plan fizzled out. It fizzled out everywhere except Indiana, that is, where neither churches nor umbrellas were great enough to contain the faithful, who instead thronged to gymnasiums and arenas for thirty-two minute weeknight services complete with live bands, popcorn, cheerleaders – and no collection plate! The One True Church of the Hoosier State was basketball, and the faithful cried out the Lord's name and prayed with a fervor that priests and pastors could only hope for on Sunday morning.

And so one by one each of the various denominations came to take up basketball. They filed it between *baptism* and *Bingo* in their catalog of spiritual practices and cited *Genesis for Hoosiers* as their authority: "The Houses of God begat teams, and the teams cleaved into leagues, and upon the land there sprang forth practices and uniforms and playoffs and games in elementary school gyms – and it was Good."

Our junior high league consisted of Protestant churches only. This was for the protection of the member congregations, lest a defeat on the court be interpreted as some sort of theological setback. *St. Mary's 55 – First Methodist 49* the headlines would scream. *Meatless Fridays Commence for Methodists on March 1.* We considered such a possibility unlikely from what little we knew about Catholics, but it was not a chance we were willing to take, fond of meat as we were. What we did know was that they tended to be short people prone to superstition and, hence, ill-equipped for basketball. Their game would be highlighted by much crossing and genuflecting, resulting in poor defense and frequent traveling calls, and their timeouts would be squandered with aimless idol worship. That same year I met Michael O'Hara, my first Catholic. He was a likable kid, and to my surprise, he seemed just like the rest of us in every discernible way – like the Pod People from *Invasion of the Body Snatchers.* Pretty sneaky, that Michael O'Hara.

With the Papist threat safely diverted we were able to focus on our fellow Protestants.

To us kids the various denominations were differentiated not by their beliefs but by their limitations. Methodists didn't drink. Church of God-ers didn't dance. United Pentecostals didn't believe in movies. To be more accurate, they believed that movies existed, but thought that actually seeing one was a bad idea. Everybody didn't believe in something, but nobody didn't believe in basketball.

Mom called Coach Canfield to tell him I wanted to play for First Methodist, but she also told him that I didn't really know all the rules. This was a clever ploy to lower the coach's expectations, so that I could dazzle him with my mediocrity. It was a little too clever perhaps, because in Indiana only a foreign exchange student from Mars does not know the rules of basketball. Coach Canfield concluded early on that I'd best learn the rules of the game in a spot at the end of the bench, safely away from the action.

At our first practice uniforms were distributed, and there was great ritual around selecting our numbers. We shot free throws to determine the order of choice, a process that took only slightly longer than the practice itself. Other kids snatched up the numbers of their favorite NBA players. Wilt Chamberlain and Jerry West were the first to go with Elgin Baylor not far behind. I picked out a uniform with the number 11, reasoning that the vertical numerals would make me look taller than my 5'3." On the court I would clearly be an imposing force with which to be reckoned. The gold form-fitting top looked great on me, accentuating my stylish equatorial rolls of fat. I had always considered them to be a safety feature, not unlike permanently inflated air bags. When I ran to my place on the bench, my body continued to undulate even after I was seated. I was 130 pounds of Jell-O. If I remained very still, the oscillation usually stopped by midway through the first quarter. I believe now that Coach Canfield must have thought I actually was a great serving of golden Jell-O at the end of the bench and gave me little playing time as a result.

As the season unfolded I adapted to my role on the bench. I chose to think of myself as a secret weapon to be unleashed in critical situations, such as when our unsuspecting opponent was down by twenty in the fourth quarter. To maintain the secrecy there were many games where I did not play at all. The strategy worked, for few teams felt the sting of number 11, and I ended the season with a total of four points.

The best part about that season was going home right after the games without hanging around to shower. I barely broke a sweat running from the car to the bench and back to the car. But I did get to wear the uniform, chew gum in a school gym and watch the games up close.

The season is now a blur in my memory, but our game against the ill-fated team from First Nazarene remains etched in my memory. Already suffering a savage beating at our hands, the coach put me in to finish the job with these instructions.

"You, Jell-O! Get in there!"

I played tenacious defense for several seconds before committing a foul, the foul that would give them their only point of the game against our forty-three. I was pulled out almost immediately for spoiling our shutout and remained the stealth weapon at the end of the bench for the rest of the regular season. A shutout, I learned later, would have had grave theological implications. The First Church of the Nazarene would close in shame, and at the conclusion of a long and painful conversion process their congregants would become Methodists. For the first year the converts would be confined to the front three rows of pews, which were traditionally empty anyway. It was as if we expected the minister to call on us during the service.

"As Paul told the Ephesians," he would say, peering officiously over his half glasses, "Let no one deceive you with empty words. For because of these things –"

Suddenly and without warning his full attention would turn to the front pew and those unfortunate souls who occupied it.

"Bob Deaton!" he would boom out. "According to our records, you have pledged five cents of your allowance to the church each week, yet I see that you have fallen short by twenty-five cents! You don't want to spend the rest of eternity in the fiery pits of hell for a quarter, do you, Mr. Deaton?"

"But, Reverend," I would whimper, "I put my nickel in the plate every week! I just forget to use the envelope!"

"See that you do." His gaze would fix on me until I had melted into the pew, then he would resume, never taking his eyes from the sniveling puddle that was once me. Without missing a beat he'd pick up right where he'd left off.

"– the wrath of God comes on the children of disobedience!"

Eternal damnation was not a risk I was willing to take, so I always lobbied Mom and Dad for a seat in the back of the church and wore pew-colored clothes for camouflage. I was just glad that I wasn't an Ephesian.

Soon thereafter the playoffs ensued, and we breezed through one team after another with remarkable ease. In succession we dispatched a team of creationists, another who called their minister "Father", then one that went to church on Saturday. With little difficulty we had advanced to the championship game against the non-dancers. I had found my role on the team, not as a mere bench warmer, but as a saver of seats.

"Brian, go in for Gary," Coach had said. "Jell-O, save Brian's seat."

"But why, Coach? Brian's seat isn't going anywhere."

"Jell-O, suppose I want to take Brian out of the game and put Gary back in, but President Kennedy has come in and sat down in Brian's spot. Now Brian has no place to sit, and we can't very well ask the president to move, now can we, hmmm?"

"We could all hum *Hail to the Chief* and hope he gets up," I suggested.

"Don't count on it. I've heard you guys sing in church."

"Can't Brian sit in Gary's spot?"

"Nope, because the president has brought Mrs. Kennedy with him, and she's in Gary's spot. So now we've got six men on the court because Brian can't sit down, ten if you count the Secret Service. You know what that means, Jell-O?"

"They switch to a zone defense?"

"No, it means we get a technical foul, and I don't want another 43-1 game because of a tech. You with me on this, Jell-O?"

Presidential pardons surely covered technical fouls, but I'd discuss that with the president later. To atone for my role in our 43-1 victory earlier in the season I latched on to my job as saver of seats with missionary zeal. The record book will show that my key saves propelled us to victory on more than one occasion.

As the final game with the non-dancers neared, our practices intensified. In the locker room after an especially spirited session, Coach Canfield whipped us into a frenzy that would carry us through the next several minutes.

"Who's going to win?" he yelled.

"We are!" we shouted back, demonstrating our mastery of the call and response format we'd learned in church.

"WHO'S GOING TO WIN?" he repeated.

"They are," I muttered under my breath.

Franky Franklin, the smallest kid on the team, looked at me in wonder.

"THEY ARE?" he repeated foolishly.

Franky had a valid question, but there's one thing he had yet to learn. When you hear something that could incite a riot, you don't repeat it louder than you heard it, otherwise it becomes yours. It's unnecessary self-incrimination, like saying "Excuse me" louder than you burp.

I'm pretty sure Franky learned his lesson that day though, as our teammates set upon him for his faithless pronouncement that "they", the non-dancers, were going to win, and beat him relentlessly with their towels. I was forced to join in the tumult and continued the pummeling even after all others had ceased, for standing aside would have been an obvious act of self-incrimination. I suppose abstaining could have been interpreted as an act of mercy, but that possibility did not occur to me until much, much later.

Our championship hopes ended when "they" won. I watched the game from the comfort and convenience of my usual spot at the end of the bench. It was a close game, with the golden boys from First Methodist going down to defeat by four points.

Our starting five went the distance, so I had no saves to record. Some of the guys took the loss pretty hard, but not me. I got to wear the uniform, chew gum in a school gym and watch the games up close.

Besides, I never was much of a dancer.

the big glass mountain

Coach Macy didn't much care whether I got an *A* or a *C*, and that was okay. Teaching a gym class was a mere contractual technicality for him, and we all knew it. He was here to win basketball games and nothing else. Another loss to Alexandria in the sectionals and the press would be sucking his brains out through a straw. There were persistent murmurs that he should have taken a dive off the Ninth Street Bridge the year before to atone for that 36-33 slow motion disaster. Coach was new to Indiana and unfamiliar with the protocol. Another upset like that would have the whole town guzzling Kool-Aid like it was Jonestown on a hot summer night. Only if the loss had been to Muncie Central could it have been worse.

Our emotional investment in basketball was enormous. As a kid in grade school, I listened to the games on the radio, and Mom taught me how to keep score. Two marks for a basket, one for a free throw. Pay special attention to Billy Hazard, she said. Billy was our high scorer, the one guy who could get it done. These were bleak years though, the Dark

Ages of basketball in Anderson before Coach Macy and the Renaissance. Despite his considerable talents, Billy couldn't carry the team alone, and the Indians finished a miserable 3 and 17. Years later when I was in junior high, I sat at a desk where Billy had carved his name. Nothing prepared me for the feelings I experienced. It was as if I'd unexpectedly discovered the Holy Grail under my seat. For an hour I ran my fingers over the letters of his name, oblivious to every- thing the teacher said, just as Billy Hazard probably had been years before. Ordinarily I judged such acts of vandalism harshly, but this was not vandalism. It was my connection with history. I traced Billy's name on a piece of notebook paper and revered it as if it were the shinbone of a saint. I think they retired his desk after that. Stuck it in a glass case in the gym with other sacred artifacts of Basketball.

The first year of the post-Hazard era the gym burned down. No one was hurt, and the dank old gym was replaced by a magnificent cathedral of basketball that seated 8500 rabid fans. The new cathedral was fitted with a new high priest, Coach Macy. The old priest settled into a comfortable faculty position as a Driver Ed teacher. Spending his golden years with raw green teenage drivers proved to be far less stressful than coaching basketball. Sure, he had a few dozen parents who expected him to bring their kids back alive every day, but the whole town expected him to win ball games, and few could handle pressure like that. He retired peacefully not long after, his mind remarkably intact.

Coach Macy brought us hope and excitement again. No longer were we running on the fumes of tradition, we had the real thing. His first year we went twelve and eight and were in every game going into the last three minutes.

At tournament time we decorated the living room mirror with team pictures and crepe paper streamers in an annual rite of expectancy. All of Anderson was pregnant with emotion. What was a mere reflective surface eleven months a year was transformed into an altar when February came around. Several visits a day to the mirror shrine were commonplace. In each worshipful moment I stared intently into the face of each player and saw us as state champions. By the end of the season we knew each player by name and number and could cite his scoring average to two decimal places.

Our boys usually won the sectional, the first round of the tournament, beating up on over-matched little schools that dared come into our field house with little more than hope and a cheering section. To the mirror we added a second team picture, this one of an elated team and elated cheer-leaders fresh off a sectional conquest. Cutting down the nets was a ritual reserved for the victors, and in the photo the players wore the nets around their necks like trophies of war. Posting photos of the vanquished teams and their sobbing cheerleaders was considered tacky and vengeful, unless, of course, it was Muncie Central, whose every defeat was a cause for celebration.

"Rivals" was how the newspapers charitably described us, but "archenemies" would have been more accurate. No competition with Muncie Central went by without a fight breaking out somewhere. As a ninth-grader at my very first football game, I watched the players came to blows over a roughing penalty, and the stands emptied onto the field in an act of solidarity – and insanity. I was terrified and kept a safe distance, grateful for avoiding the pounding I would have received had it been an away game.

The band broke into the national anthem in an attempt to restore order, but it was to no avail. It was a commonly held belief in Anderson that Indiana's admission into the union in 1816 was meant to exclude Muncie, but that fact had somehow been overlooked in the official paperwork. So, the national anthem served only to incite the crowd further. Now they fought for the glory of the nation, as well as Anderson High School.

Of all our competitions with Muncie Central in the next four years, only the debate team avoided coming to blows, but the rebuttals took a nasty and personal turn in the Muncie Invitational. Arguments on nuclear disarmament and verification were sprinkled with slanderous remarks about one another's schools, which quickly escalated into a vigorous discussion of mothers. Interestingly, neither team lost points for their unseemly remarks, only for their inability to support them with credible sources.

"Mr. Moderator, I have in my hand this highly classified Pentagon study on Defense Preparedness in which Muncie Central High School was ranked worst in the nation in reading comprehension, integer addition and dental hygiene! And the girls there are all dogs, too, except for that one cheerleader."

"I beg to differ, Mr. Moderator. The statistics cited by my opponent are flawed and taken out of context, as this recent classified Atomic Energy Commission report on Nuclear

Fallout from Atmospheric Testing clearly shows. Instead, it was Anderson High School, not Muncie Central that –"

No, there was none of that – just some name calling, and then it was over. All the way home we told each other they were darned lucky that they didn't start anything, because we would have put the Big Hurt on them. And we weren't kidding either.

Basketball season ended in defeat, as it always did for all but one of the six hundred-and-some teams in the state tournament. The school was in mourning for days. We gathered in the gym for the traditional basketball memorial service. Coach Macy described our quest as climbing a glass mountain. As we near the summit, he said, sometimes we fall short and slide all the way down to where we began, and our quest begins anew with the new season.

The talk of those who came to play the game of basketball and gave their all for AHS soon gave way to "Wait until next year," and we filed out of the gym in a blue basketball funk. We remained that way until the first crocuses pushed their way out of the ground a couple of weeks later, and we could experience the redemption of spring.

dexter ellis and the shower king

After two weeks of aimless bouncing we had deserted the trampoline and moved on to basketball, the essence of high school physical education in the Hoosier state. The trampoline tour had been uneventful, except for the day that Dexter Ellis wedged his head between the springs attempting a somersault mount, but we expected that much of Dexter.

I stood poised at the starting line with the basketball in my two hands, lovingly caressing the bumps on its skin while I waited for Coach to blow the whistle. Ahead of me on the gymnasium floor was a maze of folding chairs, mocking me, challenging me to dribble my way through unscathed, but I was not to be mocked. There was not a chair out there that could defend me – although there were several that were equal offensive threats. At the sound of the whistle I was off like a jet-propelled snake, slithering my way between the chairs and returning to GO almost before I had left.

My impressive chair slalom time helped compensate for the pathetic vertical leap measurement I'd recorded the day before. Try as I might, I could not reach escape velocity, and the earth snatched me back into its grasp six inches after I had departed. By the end of five weeks of basketball though, I'd acquitted myself well. It was obvious from my performance how I had achieved secret weapon status just two years before, wearing the First Methodist gold.

It had been a good semester and I expected my grades to show it. I had honed my skills at multiple choice test-taking to laser precision. My unique content-free style of answering essay questions was a triumph of form over substance that usually resulted in full credit.

Q: Compare and Contrast the French and American Revolutions.

A: The people of America and France rose up in revolt against the repressive powers that were the root cause of their discontent. The revolutions were alike, to the extent that all revolutions are alike, yet unique to their time and place. The American Revolution was set here in America, while the French Revolution took place far across the sea in France. When the histories of the two great nations are recounted, the stories of their revolutions will be told and the leaders of each struggle will be remembered as people of renown.

Oh yeah, I was good all right. So it was with great expectation that I opened my report card. Physics – *A*, Trigonometry – *A*, World History – *A*. The string of *A*'s continued with satisfying monotony until I reached Physical Education, where the *C* stood out like catsup on a white linen Nehru jacket. A *C* in Gym? *A*'s were passed out like snuff samples at a rodeo! *B*'s were routinely given out just for showing up. Nobody gets a *C* in gym. Nobody expect maybe Dexter Ellis.

Dexter Ellis was a hapless kid with no discernible physical skills. Sure, he could walk and feed himself, but in the cutthroat world of gym glass, it takes more. Whoever first coined the phrase, "There but for the grace of God go I" surely had Dexter in mind. He was nothing less than the physical manifestation of our collective insecurity.

In our post-high school years Dexter could go on to win an Emmy, write the Great American Novel or find a cure for herpes, but none of that would matter. Just as Henry Kissinger would rather have been an all-star football player with the mind of an ant than win the Nobel Peace Prize, so it was with the rest of us, Dexter in particular. The moving finger writes and having writ moves on, and it's in high school that we get the finger, and whatever is writ goes on our Permanent Record.

Occupying the other end of the spectrum was John Steele. John had been shaving since he was in the fourth grade and was clearly in his element in the communal shower of gym class. John was the sort who would spend the best years of his life bathed in the dim glow of a 19-inch television in his brother-in-law's garage, smashing empty malt liquor cans and the occasional bottle against his sloping forehead. But at this moment, here in the shower, in the years of our lives that counted most, he was King of the Shower, and few would not have traded his dismal prospects for the awe he inspired among us less well equipped.

John Steele disappeared after graduation. Rumors persisted that he'd hitchhiked to California and become something of a minor porn film star, but that was just some girls talking. The truth was that he moved to Fort Wayne and took a job at Kroger's in the meat department.

My showers were brief and meaningless, Dexter Ellis's even more so. Dexter Ellis was the polar opposite of John Steele. He was a pudgy kid – no, he was fat; *I* was pudgy – and the only kid in class that was uncircumcised. I knew that we didn't come from the factory that way, but we all figured it was a mandatory dealer option at Saint John's Hospital. Clearly Dexter had not been born at St. John's like the rest of us, or else he had slipped away from the dinner table before the turkey was carved.

Dexter was a friend of sorts. It was an alliance of convenience that served both of us well. Against the forces of testosterone-induced group insanity, a two-nerd axis offered Dexter extra protection against a *Lord of the Flies* worst-case scenario. And as long as I was near Dexter, I was clearly not the weakest gazelle in the herd. Pathetic as I was, I looked good by contrast. Real good.

Because of our alphabetical proximity, I had convinced myself that I had received Dexter's grade. Surely no other would be rebuked with a *C* in gym, certainly not me, not with my perfect attendance and spectacular chair slalom times. It was clear that a visit to Coach was in order, but it was basketball tournament time and Coach was wound tighter than a two-dollar watch and was to be approached with caution. He could fine me a letter grade and sentence me to laps for the rest of the year just as easily as he could give me the *A* that I so richly deserved.

I'd begin with an introduction, hoping not to disparage his intelligence by telling him the obvious. He had about six hundred students, but I was pretty sure he knew the names of only the twelve on the basketball team.

"Coach, I'm Bob Deaton, as I'm sure you know."

Yeah, that would work. Now about the grade. It was unavoidable that I implicate Dexter, but I had to be careful to avoid suggesting that Coach had screwed up. The bill would be filled by the judicious use of passive voice.

"Dexter Ellis's grade seems to have been given to – no, still too direct – seems to have been received by me."

So far, so good. Now I had to establish Dexter's identity, but I could hardly drag him back to gym class for one more hellish instant.

"Dexter's the, uh, fat kid. The goofy fat kid."

No, too harsh. Besides, it wasn't nearly specific enough.

"Dexter's the one that's – he wasn't born at St. John's, and he's not like the rest of us."

No, too subtle. Coach might well assume that Dexter was dropped on his head. Better to just be direct.

"Dexter's not circumcised!"

Okay, that was good. Just get it out.

Then a sudden cold fear ran through me, warning that it might well take more than a student ID to identify which of us was Dexter, and there would be no extra points for the clean underwear that Mom thought was so important. Suddenly, the *C* I had inherited wasn't looking so bad after all. So what if Dexter had just won the lottery with my *A*? I could live with that. I would always have the memory of my spectacular chair slalom times as a consolation prize. And it was one less time I would have to undress in gym class.

taffeta and rebar

The Iceberg Ahead

Jimmy gazed at the chessboard through his Clark Kent glasses. His was the face of contentment as he slid the black bishop in for the kill.

"Check!"

My situation did not look good, down by three pieces with both king and ego exposed. He was my friend, but at that moment I hated him. Conceding was out of the question, but dumping the board in his lap was not.

"Does this mean you give up?" he asked.

"It means the game has become tedious, and I weary of playing it with you."

Jimmy claimed the victory and went on to recount his crafty moves and review my greatest blunders. He was a regular highlights reel.

"Did you know, Bob," he said, changing the subject only slightly, "that some people think we're nerds?"

"Us? You're kidding!"

"Yes, us. Outsiders with no social standing. Complete dipsticks"

"Us?"

"Hard to believe, isn't it?"

It wasn't hard to believe. I had suspected it since I was in third grade.

"But don't give up. There is still hope for us."

"I hadn't realized we were hopeless."

"Oh, yes, terminally so. Even so, there's hope."

"How can that be?"

"Because even for geeks like us, there's always a source of redemption. And do you know what that is?"

"Uh, Jesus?"

"Nope. Jesus is for when you have cancer and stuff. This is a different kind of problem."

"I give up."

"The Prom, dummy! The 1964 Junior Prom! It's our ticket out of geekdom. Go, and you are cleansed!"

"But I haven't been to a dance all year. Or ever, for that matter."

"Me neither, but that doesn't matter. This isn't a tournament. We don't have to qualify. We just have to go … and with a girl."

"I knew there was a catch."

"Are you kidding? This is like shooting ducks in a barrel! This is such a big deal to girls that they'll go with anybody!"

"Anybody?"

"Anybody!"

"Even Dexter Ellis?"

"Well, no. Dexter's in the Jesus category with cancer and tornadoes."

"But us?"

"Even you, my friend. Girls are on a social vision quest called *Titanic*. The Prom is an iceberg and we are the life-boats."

"We are?"

"We are! Just dial a number, hum a few bars of *Nearer My God to Thee* and you've got a date. It's that easy."

"Ducks in a barrel?"

"In a barrel!"

"Why is this so important to them?"

"No one knows. That's the way it is in the Land of Girls, Bob. They're not like us. They're not just soft boys, you know. They're … girls!"

It was a strange land, this Land of Girls, and I was about to wander in with no passport or book of foreign phrases. Worse yet, my guide was the captain of the chess team.

"Do you have a date?" I asked.

"Not exactly. I'm going to call Patsy McClellan tonight and give her the good news."

"Patsy McClellan? That's the best a stud like you can do? I think I'd just toss her a lifejacket and keep that seat open in the lifeboat."

"I'm not the first lifeboat into the water, you know."

"Which means?"

"Which means anybody you'd want to take has had a Prom date since February."

"I though this was ducks in a barrel."

"Some days, my friend, you're the lifeboat, and some days you're the duck."

Mugwumps and Manifest Destiny

Why it was called the *Junior* Prom was a mystery to me. I promised myself that one day I'd devote an afternoon to matters I'd put off too long – understanding the intricacies of crop rotation, learning the second verse of *The Star Spangled Banner*, and, of course, unraveling the etymology of the Junior Prom. But for now all I needed to know was that only juniors and seniors from Anderson High School were allowed to attend. Girls couldn't bring their fiancés who were home on leave before shipping out to Viet Nam. Guys couldn't bring their aspiring super-model cousins from New Castle and pass them off as long-distance girlfriends. It was just an Anderson High School family affair. Outsiders need not apply. No ringers allowed.

This was The Real Thing of the spring season, bigger than a royal wedding, more important than an inaugural ball, second only to basketball in the grand scheme of things. The social pressure was enormous. Even though the Prom held no particular appeal for me, I felt strangely compelled to go. A lifetime of resisting peer pressure had left me unprepared for this. "If everyone wore poop on their heads, would you?" my mother would ask, and now that it was Prom season I would have to answer, "Yes, Yes! And make mine a double scoop!"

The Prom Committee was given the daunting task of transforming the gym into a place of wonder with an atmosphere suitable for a formal dance on a lunch money budget. A couple of stolen one-way street signs, a meter maid and a handful of pigeons might have transformed the gym into a microcosm of downtown Anderson, but *Daring Downtown* as a prom theme would have been dead on arrival, Petula Clark's opinion to the contrary. Downtown was just no place to spend an evening. Instead the committee opted for the sentimental favorite, *Camelot*. With a decorating budget scarcely adequate for a few rolls of crepe paper and an abundance of darkness and imagination, the gym would become seventh-century England.

There was a sense that the whole affair was contrived by and for girls, much the same way that Grandparents Day and wedding anniversaries were conspiracies of the greeting card companies. Still, there was no getting out of it. It was a social riptide, and the lifeguard was off-duty, working his own Prom plans.

My target of opportunity was Nancy Carmendale. By alphabetical serendipity, she sat next to me in U.S. History class and was the focus of my unrequited lust. For weeks I'd mulled over my strategy. It was common knowledge that she had a boyfriend at another school. I envisioned him as Godzilla without the charm, ready to clobber anyone hitting on his girlfriend or even entertaining impure thoughts. By those criteria, no one was safe. We routinely entertained impure thoughts about any female with opposable thumbs. Still, Godzilla was ineligible to take her, and staying home surely would not be an option for her. What could be better, I reasoned, than for her to go with a hapless geek like me? Despite my considerable charms, which had seemingly been hidden in a safe place and were now inaccessible to me, I was harmless – a little too harmless apparently. Seconds before U.S. History began, I blurted out my proposal.

"So, hey, you wanna go to the Prom with me?"

She looked at me as if she had come to Lourdes in search of the miraculous, and I was the consolation prize, a sorry vision that proclaimed, "Okay, everybody go on home. No miracles here tonight. Move along now."

Her response was noncommittal, more like a cough than a "Yes, I'd love to!" I took it to mean that she'd think it over.

Each day while Mr. Pennyworth droned on about Mugwumps and Manifest Destiny, I gazed expectantly in her direction waiting for her decision. Maybe *yes* was implicit in her cough, but I was reluctant to ask her again. "Hey, I was about to say *yes,*" she would say, "but if you're going to pester me about it, then forget it!" Still, I had to know. To prevent any awkward conversation that would surely follow, I timed my question to within seconds of the bell.

"Hey, Nancy, remember I asked you to the Prom a few weeks ago?"

"You did? Oh, I'm not going."

The next morning homeroom president Winslow Cotton delivered the first in a series of degrading announcements designed to inspire us to buy our share of Prom tickets.

"Only two days left to get your Prom tickets. You all got your tickets? Anyone out there without a date?"

The dateless among us assumed postures of invisibility, like a Jehovah's Witness during the pledge of allegiance, and waited for the moment to pass.

"No? Good. I'd hate to think about pathetic losers —"

"Thank you, Winslow," Miss Esterhazy interrupted. "You can sit down now."

" — who can't even get a date —"

"Sit down, Winslow."

" – to the most important –"

"SIT DOWN!"

Winslow shut up and sat down, chastised but confident that he'd made his point. Winslow had his constituency to be sure, but he was generally not well liked. Miss Esterhazy had appointed him to fill out the term of the charismatic Jackie Birdwell, who without prior notice dropped out of school, got married on a Wednesday night and moved to Texas to escape the storks that were circling her house.

The psychological warfare ratcheted up over the next three days. It was Friday now, just eight days before the Prom, and Monday was the last day that tickets were on sale.

The Lessons of History

Nancy Carmendale's footprints were all over my shattered ego, and seeing her in Mr. Pennyworth's class made me more depressed with each passing day.

"Those who do not learn the lessons of history," Mr. Pennyworth rattled on in the background, "are doomed to repeat its mistakes." I was still staring wistfully in Nancy's direction when the bell rang.

"Bob, what are the lessons of history that you've learned?"

Mr. Pennyworth's question was a punch thrown after the bell had ended the round – definitely against the rules.

"Uh, I dunno … Keep your powder dry?" Mom sure didn't like it when her powder got wet.

Mentally I added "And never ask Nancy Carmendale out to anything again!" I could have said it right out loud, and it wouldn't have mattered. Anything said after the bell couldn't have been used against me. Wasn't that what that new Miranda thing was all about?

He bore in on me with his history teacher eyes. "I advise you to give it some thought."

I didn't want to give it some thought. I wanted to think about Nancy Carmendale and feel sorry for myself.

Later that day I had a chance encounter with Karen Kupchek, universal object of wide-eyed slobbering desire and my personal obsession since eighth grade. All thoughts of Nancy Carmendale and the lessons of history were driven from my mind.

"Mr. Pennyworth wants to talk to you," she said coolly. "He found out that you don't have a Prom date."

I hadn't spoken with Karen since my unfortunate gas attack in ninth grade biology. I was hoping she had discovered a reason of her own to talk to me, but I would have to save that experience for another lifetime.

"Mr. Pennyworth's keeping the Official Loser List now? I thought that was Winslow Cotton's job."

"No," she sniffed. "Anything to do with your Permanent Record is a faculty issue."

While I lay there bleeding, she got right to the point.

"Mr. Pennyworth thinks you should go with Evelyn Wadbury."

"Huh?"

"Look, he wants to see his favorite students go to the Prom. For whatever reason that seems to include you," she yawned. "Evelyn's expecting your call."

"But I don't know her. What's she like?"

"She's, uh… she's like you—Oops! Look at the time, will you?" she said with a glance at her bare wrist. "Gotta go now! Let's do this again next year!"

And with that Karen Kupchek, goddess of the junior class, faded into the milieu of students, leaving me panicked, yet strangely aroused.

Evelyn was like me? What did that mean? An *A* student? I'd never seen her at any of the usual places – Chess club, Debate team, Science club. Maybe she was one of those right-brain *A* students, the Latin club type.

Ducks In A Barrel

Evelyn Wadbury … Evelyn Wadbury. I couldn't place the name, but Nancy Carmendale knew her. Even though Nancy had only recently wrenched the still-beating heart from my chest and danced on it with casual indifference, I was willing to let bygones be bygones. I needed information.

"So, what's she like, this Evelyn Wadbury?"

"She's nice," Nancy said. "Very nice."

"No, what does she *look* like?"

"Um, medium height, blondish hair. She's, uh, nice!"

Why didn't she have Prom plans at this late date, I wondered. Surely there was a logical explanation. Evelyn was perhaps a girl of indescribable splendor, a girl so hot that every guy in school would have been too intimidated to approach her. Medium height? Blond hair? Nice? That could only mean one thing. Brigitte Bardot had transferred to our school to hang out incognito. It was the Anderson High

School witness protection program for French film celebrities looking for a little R & R between movies.

I polled a number of kids. None of the guys seemed to know who Evelyn was, but the girls did and all gave me the same answer. "She's nice!" There was no denying that Brigitte Bardot was nice. I'd seen John Steele staring at her movie poster down at the Paramount Theater and moaning, "Mmmmmm, nice!" You can tell a lot about a woman from her movie poster.

The possibilities weighed heavily on me for the next two days. Evelyn was a sure thing, reserved exclusively for me by Mr. Pennyworth, but taking someone I knew would be far less risky, even if the upside potential were something less than Brigitte Bardot. With a sure thing in my pocket, I could risk a little rejection. It was Sunday night, only hours before Winslow Cotton would make Prom tickets available to us last-minute losers for the final time.

I started with Janet Meese. She'd had a crush on me in the seventh grade for reasons that still elude me. I wouldn't hold her bad taste against her now. There was plenty of time for that later.

"Hello, Janet? This is Bob Deaton … Deaton … D-E-A-T-O-N. You got a date for the Prom? No? Great! Wanna go with me? You don't? Uh, do you think maybe your sister would? Hello? Hello?"

Next up was Della Perry, who was equally resistant to my overtures. She added that her sister Becky might be interested, but she was already asleep. Her bedtime was 9:00 PM until she was in the fourth grade. Before I could decline, the line went dead. I hoped Becky wouldn't be expecting my call.

Third on the list was Judy French, who was pretty sure she had a prior engagement. Batting cleanup was Marie Nicoletto, a girl who had no plans for the upcoming weekend, but when she did, they wouldn't involve the Prom or me. Somewhere along the way I also hit a wrong number, a girl from another school who had confused me with someone more desirable, but only momentarily.

That left Evelyn Wadbury. It was late now, but I suspected she'd be up waiting hopefully by the phone. Answering on the first ring would mean that she was desperate, a bad sign. But if she were as smart as she was desperate, she would probably hold out until the second or maybe even the third ring.

Then again a first ring answer could imply that she was supremely confident, aware of the obvious implications but above it all. Supreme confidence is not a gift lightly bestowed upon teens, and never without good reason. Brigitte Bardot would answer on the first ring.

The phone had barely completed its first ring when I heard a voice on the other end.

"Hello-o-o" a female voice answered cheerfully.

"Evelyn?"

"Yes?" I couldn't tell if it was confidence or desperation in her voice, but it definitely wasn't French. I could still hope for Elke Sommer.

"This is Bob Deaton."

"Oh, hi! It's so nice to talk to you!"

Nothing in my limited experience with girls had prepared me for such an enthusiastic response. I wondered what they'd told her about me.

"I understand you don't have a date for the Prom." My approach may have been a little too "Jack Webb" for the occasion, but this was, after all, a sure thing. Ducks in a barrel.

"That's right," came her cheery response. With each successive breath her level of expectation became ever more evident. To my surprise, hers was not the voice of impending rejection, and for a moment I toyed with switching roles. "I'm not going either. Bye." I'd wait just long enough to hear her gasp, then hang up. To play it safe I'd leave the phone off the hook.

I savored the fantasy, then returned to the original script, the one that went "Wanna go with me? Yes, I'd love to, blah, blah, blah."

We endured a few more minutes of pleasantries before she remarked about a composition I'd written for English on composer Claude Debussy. The teacher had liked it so much she gave me an *A* and read it to Evelyn's class. My theme was a masterpiece of deception. The assignment was to write a thousand-word piece with four references. Mine was a scant three hundred words, and one of my references was the liner notes from a record album. My mom, normally a person of considerable integrity, was a willing co-conspirator. She typed it for me, triple-spaced with two inch margins to complete the illusion that it was a tome of some significance, or at least heft. With her artistry the Cliff Notes for a Shakespeare sonnet could have been transformed into *War and Peace* and no one would have been the wiser. It was pure alchemy how a little typing trickery and a pair of thick-lensed safety glasses with tortoise shell frames could combine to give me the illusion of intelligence.

Evelyn and I talked a bit more, mostly about me, then agreed to meet the next morning by the stairwell. The girls were right. She was nice.

The Beginning of Destiny

The next morning I began my descent into Hell with Winslow Cotton as my escort.

"Today's the last day for you last-minute losers to get your Prom tickets. Is there anyone here –" He paused and fixed his gaze on me. "– so pathetic and desperate that they've waited until today?"

"WINSLOW!" Miss Esterhazy scolded.

If I were ever cornered in a barn by rabid wolves and Miss Esterhazy was looking on with a shotgun, I could only hope that she would not wait until they'd taken the first couple of bites out of me before filling their scummy hides with lead. I furtively handed a twenty to Winslow and mumbled something about "finally getting my schedule conflict resolved." I didn't look around, but I'm pretty sure everyone bought it.

My first period economics class dragged through an endless discussion of monetary policy. My mind was still all abuzz with thoughts of the Federal Reserve System when I heard the voice behind me on the stairwell.

"Bob Deaton?" It sounded familiar. It sounded … nice. I turned to discover that its owner was a slightly pudgy girl, blond, with thick glasses and an exuberant outbreak of acne. Surely she would take me to her luscious friend Evelyn, who was being kept in a secluded castle far away – but within the Anderson School District – to prevent mortals from gazing upon her countenance and turning themselves into pond creatures, or at the very least mindlessly driving their cars into the rocks in White River.

"I'm Evelyn."

There had been some terrible mistake. She was not Brigitte Bardot. She was not Elke Sommer. She was – ME! A feminine version to be sure, but she was my doppelganger, my opposite sex identical twin who had emerged from another dimension to rescue me from social ignominy. Didn't Mr. Pennyworth appreciate how deeply superficial I was? My wish was for a girl who was more … distracting. I didn't care if she wanted to be cremated and have her ashes scattered at the mall when she was gone, as long as she lit my fire in the mean time.

At the sound of the bell I bolted for my next class, resigned to my fate. The train had left the station, and I was under it.

Evelyn's reaction to me may well have been the same, but it wasn't a possibility I was willing to consider. I had, after all, written the Debussy masterpiece, and that made me quite a catch. If only Nancy Carmendale had read my Debussy paper.

The Fins Go Down

The next four days consumed me with preparation. With reluctance my vocabulary grew to include unwelcome visitors like *cummerbund* and *nosegay*. The visit to Tony's Tux and

Formal Shoppe marked my descent into the next level of Hell. I had the dubious honor of being served by Tony himself. Tony was a man of middle years whom hope had long since abandoned. It was clear from his demeanor that he had seen one too many kids this Prom season and heard his wares described as "monkey suits" one too many times.

I shuffled into the feet outlined on the floor in front of the mirror and did as I was instructed. Here was a man, I imagined, who could assess a neck size at a glance and fashion a noose from a tape measure in my exact dimensions. Such a man was not to be trifled with.

He gathered my measurements in every direction, pausing occasionally to pat me and make unintelligible sounds of contempt. I began to wish I'd gone to Hollywood Outfitting instead. Everyone knew that their merchandise was shoddy and overpriced, but in exchange for dressing you like a corpse at a county funeral, they'd give you a modicum of respect.

At long last Tony handed me a pile of garments and instructed me to put them on, offering no suggestions about how it might be done. I struggled into the pieces that I recognized, leaving behind what appeared to be a satin back brace. In an attempt to match the posters that lined his walls, I wrapped the mystery garment around my waist.

"Which way do these fin things go?" I asked.

"The pleats, or 'fin things' as you prefer to call them," he sniffed, "go down. The purpose of the cummerbund is to accentuate and highlight your ... "

Tony paused to appraise the contours of my pear-shaped body. "They go down," he sighed.

The Little Shop Of Flowers

Taking care of Evelyn's flowers was all that remained on my list. I had supposed that would be a simple business, like picking a nice spring bouquet from the array of allergens that flourished in our backyard. Even a fistful of dandelions would have passed in the darkness of the gym, but Evelyn's insistence that it be free of aphids and bumblebees drove me to the flower shop. I soon learned that there were more ways to garnish a girl with flowers than there were to decorate a float in the Rose Parade. Evelyn indicated that a wrist corsage or small nosegay would be acceptable. While the word *nosegay* meant nothing to me, I was told that it would be meaningful to someone less ignorant, like a florist. She gave me an address, telling me, "Go there. He'll be expecting you."

The flower shop was a small affair nestled away on a side street. The window shades were closed, and as I approached, the door cracked open to reveal a pair of eyes.

"Password?" Eyes said in an unfamiliar accent.

"Uh, nosegay?"

"Are you being alone?"

"Well, yeah ..."

"Come!" he commanded, as the door swung open to reveal a perfectly ordinary, although darkened, flower shop.

"What is being your preference? Wrist, shoulder, waist or breast?"

"I usually go with the drumstick."

"Then you are taking chicken to the dance?"

If the chicken were a junior or senior at Anderson High School, I'm sure I would have been.

"Wrist!" I answered confidently, recalling part two of the password into the flower kingdom.

"Come back three days," he said, scribbling my order. "Go now."

I paused in the doorway to glance back before I left. "How come you don't have any windows?"

"Because I am creature of the night!" He laughed for a moment, a moment too long really. Noticing my discomfort he said, "Because my flowers, they like the darkness. I am not being vampire. Not really."

With some trepidation I returned the day of the Prom to pick up my order. We repeated the same password protocol, but this time he wouldn't let me in. Instead he pushed a stunning bouquet into my hands, saying, "Take! Take! They being free for you. Now go!"

As I walked away I could hear his voice, this time devoid of any accent.

"Hi, Darlin'. This is Uncle Will. Bob just left with your flowers. I think you're going to like 'em!"

Starch and Other Lessons

When I was about eight years old Mom appeared on a TV quiz show in Indianapolis and won a lifetime supply of starch. Dozens of boxes languished in our pantry for years, oozing a mysterious white powder from every seam. As far as I know we never used any or even opened a box in ten years. Eventually, we came to realize that we were not starch people and disposed of them.

And so, my limited experience with starch left me unprepared for the shirt that came with the tuxedo. Its front panels were petrified, possibly in dread of its fate that evening, and my search for the hidden cardboard came up empty. This was a shirt like no other garment ever to grace my body. "Stiff" does not begin to describe a garment capable of repelling bullets fired at close range. And while invulnerability was a nice feature, it was secondary at best. The highly starched shirt was primarily a structural element designed to hold the wearer in place should he fall asleep while dancing. No one has much fun while wearing a tux, appearances to the contrary, so the likelihood of dozing off rises considerably.

I painstakingly donned the remaining items just as Tony had instructed me, taking extra care to refer to the cummerbund as "pleated." The starched shirt bowed severely outward when I sat down, giving the impression that a tuxedo monster was about to burst from my chest. A couple of well-placed safety pins tamed the wild shirt, but left me with a four-star wedgie when I bent over. Jerry Lewis claimed to have never sat down in a pair of tuxedo pants, and now I knew why. Elegance was a pain in the butt.

At long last all the pieces were in place, and I surveyed my reflection in the mirror, trying on a David Niven devil-may-care sidelong smirk. The transformation was remarkable. I had gone from Bob Deaton, hapless geek, to Bob Deaton, hapless geek in a tuxedo. I was on my way.

Mom blathered on and on about how handsome I was, blathering long enough to lose all credibility. I hung around briefly for the obligatory array of pictures, then bolted for the door. My escape was almost good when Mom caught me.

"Bobby! Wait a minute!"

"Yes?"

"Do you know how to dance?"

"Uh, well, no, not really."

"You're going to the Prom without knowing how to dance? Don't you think you might need to know that sometime tonight?"

"I dunno. Yeah, I guess so."

I honestly hadn't considered it until that very moment. Getting a date was the hard part. I hadn't given too much thought to what might happen while I was on that date. Mr. Pennyworth had arranged the date. Maybe he'd be there with some last minute dance instruction for me. He'd be the guy handing out parachutes as we jumped blindly into the night.

"Come here. Let me show you," Mom said. She put on the *Best of Mantovani* album, and I felt myself descend to the next level of hell. I had planned to save it for later, but here I was going down before I even left the house.

"You put your arms here, she puts her arms there, and you move with the music, like this. See? Nothing to it."

We swayed in place for a few excruciating moments, just long enough to acquire the all-important skill of maintaining close proximity while causing no visible damage.

"Okay, got it, Mom. Thanks. Gotta go now."

I didn't expect to be getting any closer to Evelyn than I did to Mom, and I was confident I could replicate the primitive moves I'd mastered just moments before. I was on my way. Again.

As I drove off I asked myself, breathes there a woman with soul so dead that she could resist the allure of a tuxedoed geek in a green 1962 Rambler station wagon, a fresh graduate from Mom's Express Dance School earlier that very same evening? I thought not. Mesmerizing Evelyn with my newly unleashed charm was not my objective though. We were a symbiotic pair, who would be strutting and fretting our hours on the dance floor, until our passport of social validity was stamped.

Taffeta And Rebar

I arrived at Evelyn's house while it was still daylight and was greeted by a generic mom in a big pink housedress. Immediately behind her was Evelyn, motioning for me to enter. I stepped in past Big Pink and glanced back and forth at the two Wadbury women. There was no doubt that they hadn't switched babies at the hospital.

"Mom, this is Bob."

I stuck out my hand in introduction, but she took a step back and said, "Oh, just look at you!" When my mom said that it meant there was spaghetti sauce on my new white corduroys, but Big Pink's intent was less clear.

"Yes," I said agreeably. "Just look at me!"

Her scrutiny and the bouquet I clutched self-consciously in my hands conspired to make me feel like a reluctant bride on wedding day. I shoved the flowers in Evelyn's direction, hoping for a small serving of relief.

"Here. These are for you."

"Oh, thanks," she smiled. "I see you met Uncle Will."

"Uh, yeah …"

"He didn't do an animal sacrifice while you were there, did he?"

"That's enough about Uncle Will, Dear," Big Pink interjected. "You know he's been doing much better since he was released."

"Released?"

Before I could get an answer, Evelyn's father materialized from that other dimension where parents live. His resemblance to the florist was striking, but his proportions were greater, and in a way that was frightening rather than jolly.

"Come here, you two," Hoss said, bypassing the introductions. "Let me get your picture."

Yes, I thought, photograph your daughter and this geekboy in their Prom costumes, struggling futilely for a degree of normalcy that would continue to elude them even on this most special evening of the social calendar. His Polaroid camera did all it could with the subjects it had and ejected the picture into the eager hands of Big Pink, who alternately waved it and blew on it in that placebo process universally believed to hasten developing. She looked upon the emerging image with a misplaced satisfaction. He followed immediately with a shot of Evelyn alone, and before it had completely dried, stuck it into my jacket pocket.

"Bring her home the way you found her, boy," he said. "Here's a reminder."

I suppose I should have been flattered to be considered any sort of manly threat, however remote, but I wasn't. He would have been reassured to know that my plan was to make only the minimum required contact with his daughter and get her home well before channel six signed off with *The Star*

Spangled Banner. I did take notice of the way I found her though, just as one takes notice of the emergency exits on an airplane before takeoff.

Her dress was a pastel engineering marvel, a beaded profusion of acres of taffeta circumscribing a radius great enough to keep her dance partner at bay. Beneath the taffeta were all manner of womanly structural supports, most likely fiberglass with steel beams or perhaps rebar. Somewhere in Middle America there is a prom dress warehouse. In vast rows sit molded bulletproof formals of a single size, into which a new crop of eager young women will pour themselves each spring.

"Okay, one more," Hoss ordered. He pushed the shutter release repeatedly but no picture was forthcoming.

"Damn! I'm out of film! Hold that pose while I reload."

We stood frozen in cheese mode, while Hoss ran from the room in pursuit of more ammunition for the Polaroid with Big Pink scampering right behind. With no words exchanged between us, Evelyn and I took their cue and ran like overdressed rabbits to the car. We made a clean escape with no visible damage other than the spreading stain of the Polaroid in my tuxedo pocket.

As I drove away I could see Hoss in the rear view mirror furiously shooting at us with his impotent Polaroid and hear Big Pink shouting the standard parental safety warnings. I speed-shifted into second, coaxing an anemic chirp from the back tires of the Rambler and took comfort from the image of Big Pink and Hoss receding into the distance in my side-view mirror. I purposely disregarded the warning that "Objects may be closer than they appear."

Procession of the Tamenellas

Every day at 11:35 AM the southeast doors of the gym swung open for lunch, and the turbulent flow of students into the cafeteria grew into a class six rapids. Crowd theory experts flew in from Pamplona each year to observe the Running of the Students at Anderson High School. The sight of 2100 students doing the forty in under five seconds held an allure that no track or football coach could resist either, and the first week of school was set aside for a draft from the lunch runners. The crowd theorists conducted experiments to determine whether crowd speed was correlated with the quality of the lunch, only to learn that "quality" was not an attribute that applied to school cafeteria cuisine. What they failed to realize was we did not run because the food was scarce or edible. We ran because everyone else did.

And now there we were again, pouring two-by-two into the darkened confines of the gym, all for one reason – because everyone else was doing it. Moving at this speed was a new and surreal experience. I found myself awash in a sea of taffeta and beehive hairdos, of perfume and industrial strength hairspray, of stiff smiles and strained greetings, and of a hundred guys like me in rigid black tuxedoes, no more prepared for a formal dance than they were to host a Labor Day telethon. As far as I could see in every direction was the unfamiliar sight of cleavage, the result of young breasts constrained and contorted within their fiberglass prisons. I found it mystifying that girls who were normally objects of my lust had transformed themselves into glamorous versions of their mothers and now held no appeal for me. We presented our tickets of social acceptability, and the crowd moved us in a dignified fashion out onto the floor of the gym.

The transformation of the gym was remarkable. What had once been a sacred cathedral of basketball seating 8500 congregants for weekly thirty-two minute services was now profaned by a profusion of crepe paper and parachutes. On stage was a band of aging musicians who during the course of the evening would not play one recognizable tune, not even the requests. It was as if the Prom committee had brought in a plain white box labeled "music" and opened it on the stage like cheap air freshener.

Prom protocol dictated that we conduct a continuous promenade around the gym and repeat the same conversation until either the clock struck midnight or we became insane.

"Oh, Evelyn," Tamenella would gush, "Your dress is so beautiful!"

"Oh, Tamenella, so is yours!" Evelyn would gush back, "And I love your hair!"

Tamenella's date and I would nod and exchange wan smiles in silent acknowledgment of our roles as props in Ken and Barbie's Prom. The Tamenellas came one after the other, all reading from the same script. After every few Tamenellas Evelyn and I would make a pilgrimage to the cafeteria where punch and cookies had replaced the usual meat loaf. The punch was a delicious concoction of 7Up, the same drink Mom administered when I had stomach flu, and unidentifiable floating objects, some of which were said to have nutritional value. In the spirit of the evening, we chose to overlook those rumors. The cookies were mediocre, scarcely better than communion wafers, so it was no great loss to find that the pockets of my tux jacket would hold no more than two or three of them.

An air of gentility from which we could not escape had descended upon us like a great smothering cloud of mustard gas. We hated ourselves for our part in it. At least the boys did.

I ran into Jimmy there at the punch bowl, where he had just contended unsuccessfully with two other guys for the last communion cookie. His date, Patsy McClellan, wandered off with Evelyn in search of some dignity. Jimmy looked like hell, and I needed some answers.

"Are you having fun?" I asked.

"Fun?" he snorted. "That's not why we're here, Bob. We're here because it's good for us."

"It is?"

"Yeah, it's just one of those things like getting polio shots. It's no fun, but everybody has to do it."

I wasn't getting it. Would I be acquiring an immunity to formal dances?

Jimmy looked around to make sure the girls weren't listening. "It's our ticket out of geekdom. Remember?"

"Hmm, is it working?"

Patsy returned to drag him away to the dance floor and he could only shrug.

"Too soon to tell," he croaked. "Sometimes it takes a while." We were tuxedoed zombies caught in the Procession of the Tamenellas and counting the hours until the evening would end.

Thanks to my resourceful tactics, Evelyn and I were three hours on the floor before executing our first dance. Whenever a dance threat was imminent I skillfully diverted her attention with one clever ploy or another. "It was from this very spot that Bedrick hit that last second shot to take Muncie down by two points." After exhausting the past basketball season, I reached back for highlights from the previous two, with an occasional reference to the championship season of 1946. Where facts and details were hazy, I freely invented them. "Johnny Morgan used to sweat so much that he was once ejected from a game for excessive moisture." Scheherazade had nothing on me.

My dance avoidance strategy was based upon frequent trips to the punchbowl and, consequently, the restroom. My tactics were working beautifully until Evelyn sprang a surprise attack when I returned from one particularly lengthy stay.

"You don't know how to dance, do you!" she charged.

"Of course I do! I've just been waiting for the right song!"

"Well, this is it," she said, snatching me into her arms.

The song dragged on endlessly but I kept my focus by staring down at the artistry of my footwork. Not since I was a baby in my crib did the movement of my feet hold such fascination for me. Except for the occasional collision, I was scarcely aware of Evelyn. As the dance wore on though, the hardened bodice of her formal pummeled me relentlessly. I was suddenly thankful for the starch in my shirt, for without it I would have gone home a mass of bruises. When the music stopped I stepped back and rubbed my chest.

"Nothing personal," I said, "but I feel like I'm dancing with a rock."

"Well, you're no Fred Astaire yourself!" she said, looking at the fresh scuff marks on her shoes.

"That's not what I meant," I said. The scuff marks were most impressive though. "What do you have in there anyway?" I asked, nodding at her bosom.

"Just me," she smiled coyly.

"I don't get around much, but I thought girls were supposed to be softer than that. I feel like I'm in the basement of a Turkish prison kissing you through two inches of glass."

"Then I guess we'd better stay out of Turkish prisons."

As soon as the word "kiss" escaped my lips Evelyn's eyebrows shot up, and I instantly regretted my analogy. Kissing her was not part of the social contract, and I didn't want to plant that idea. It was already bad enough that our conversation had just entered her clothing.

"It's almost midnight," she said. "We've been her long enough, don't you think?"

"I'm glad we're thinking alike," I said. Relief was on the way. I could have Evelyn home and be in my own bed in twenty minutes, eighteen if I got all the lights.

"So, where are you taking me to eat?" she said sweetly.

The elevator to Hell had just descended another floor.

Live Cargo

The discomfort of the past several hours was now replaced by a festering grumpiness, although Evelyn remained annoyingly cheerful. My plans for a quick getaway were withering faster than yesterday's nosegay. Social Convention demanded that we eat, and since violators of the Social Convention were not regarded kindly, we would comply.

These were the days before chain restaurants imposed their bland uniformity upon the American landscape. McDonald's had opened in Anderson just two years before, and their sign read "Over 300 Million Sold." Burgers were fifteen cents, fries a dime. There were no Happy Meals. Happiness was a singular pursuit and the restaurants stayed out of it.

Frisch's Big Boy with its two convenient locations, one downtown and a drive-in out on Broadway, didn't serve happiness either, but at least the drive-in served *cool*. The downtown location served the dining needs of the indiscriminate. In other words, the *in* Frisch's was out and the *out* Frisch's was in. The whole Frisch's protocol was governed by a complex set of rules from the unwritten *Style Guide for Anderson Teens.* Eating inside at the *out* Frisch's was anathema and reserved for those over twenty-five and the socially brain-dead, which were pretty much the same crowd. The *raison d'être* for the *out* Frisch's was not food. Food was available anywhere, even at home, as our mothers frequently reminded us. No, the *out* Frisch's was where we gathered to see and be seen. Cruising through Frisch's was a ritual of the young, and now and then we even ate there. The *Style Guide* also required that we back into the parking slots to better observe the parade of cars that rumbled through.

We rode in silence away from the gym in quest of the dining experience that would put the stamp of completion on the evening. With no perceptible urging from me, the car followed its natural migration route out Broadway toward Frisch's. All pretense of rational thought had long since disappeared. I was a tired and grumpy guy hauling live cargo with serious dining needs.

"So, where do you want to eat?" I asked.

"Oh, I don't know. You pick a place."

"No, *you* pick a place."

"No, really. *You* pick a place." She seemed to cling to the notion that she was on a date with a gentleman who wanted nothing more than to show her a good time and had the wherewithal to make it happen.

"Look," I said, "if you don't pick a place, we're going home."

"Okay, how about Peach's Pancake Cottage?"

Pancakes were good around the clock, but I'd never heard of Peach's, and it sounded just a little too cozy.

"Forget it. We're going to Frisch's."

In an extreme act of will, I drove past the *out* Frisch's and made a U-turn back toward town. It was a safe bet that no one I knew would be there. It would be packed with second-shift assembly line workers loading up on biscuits and sausage gravy, capping it off at home with a six pack and some late night TV. In twenty years our class reunion would be held there every night, Monday through Friday. But for now, my anonymity was guaranteed.

Third Street Bridge

A couple of punks stood in the entryway to Frisch's, blocking our way. They were older guys, maybe nineteen or twenty, and emitted a vague sense of danger. One was two or three days overdue on a shave. His buddy was clean-faced and clenched a toothpick savagely between his teeth. They gave me the up and down, and stared at my tuxedo in obvious admiration.

"Hey, Stick," Toothpick said. "Where's there a fifteen cent place around here?"

I had no idea what he was talking about or what "Stick" meant, but there was nothing to be had in Anderson at one a.m. for fifteen cents, not even a wink and a smile from a desperate late-night party girl with affection for rent. Not that I would know about stuff like that.

"Hmmm, not around here," I said rubbing my chin for effect. "Not at this hour."

"Let's blow this pop stand," said Stubble. "Let's go to Muncie."

"How do we get out of this town? Huh, Stick?" asked Toothpick.

"Uh, you want highway 32. Take Third Street, which becomes 32. But that's on the other side of White River, so first you go down that way to Third Street to the bridge and then you go across the river and then you keep going and look for a sign..." My rambling explanation was accompanied by random gestures of direction, one suggesting a wrong-way turn up a one-way street, another routing them to Muncie by way of Noblesville.

"Yeah, yeah, we got it." Stubble and Toothpick disappeared into the night in the midst of my explanation, putting my babbling to a merciful end. In place of the expected "thank you" came only random mumblings about the Third Street Bridge. I admired them, for their evening had purpose, unlike mine, whose theme had now morphed from *Camelot* to *Escape From Devil's Island*.

We settled into a booth across from each other in the biscuit and sausage gravy section and ordered Big Boys. Minutes passed with each of us locked in our own inner worlds. It wasn't until the food arrived that resuming conversation was a possibility. The tartar sauce coating the sizzling beef patties was a savory combination of natural flavors and inert ingredients, and we found it curiously soothing. Evelyn's tongue loosened first.

"There's no bridge on Third Street."

"So?"

"So, you told those guys to go out Third Street over the bridge. There's no bridge on Third Street. Third Street dead-ends into the river"

"I said that?"

If only there were enough time to take Evelyn home and get back downtown, the evening might yet be salvaged. I'd never seen two punks drive a car into the river. The idea was even more delicious than the inert ingredient sauce dripping onto the sleeve of my rental tux. I could almost hear their gurgly calls for help. "Hey, Stick! Can ya help us? Huh, Stick? Can ya?"

I flicked the sauce from my sleeve and sneaked a glance at my watch. One-thirty AM. I hadn't been up this late since New Year's Eve. Wasn't there some social mercy rule that would let me escape? A clause that decreed time had run out on my date and I had to go home, finished or not? I was beginning to suspect that some starry-eyed girl at the Prom had wished that this night would never end, and that her wish had been granted by a Good Fairy, or at least a fairy with good intentions, and I was caught in the collateral damage.

My only hope lay in being arrested for a curfew violation. The law forbade anyone under eighteen from roaming the streets of Anderson after eleven PM, but it was rarely enforced. My arrest opportunities would only improve if the police knew that I'd sent two guys to the bottom of White River, even if they were just punks. I eyed a cop a few tables away, hunkered down over a large plate of biscuits with sausage gravy, and I formulated my confession.

From the depths of my reveries I heard a voice say "Can you take me home?"

"Huh?" I said, looking around for the voice's owner.

"Can you take me home now?" Evelyn said. "It's not that I'm not having a good time, but you're keeping me out pretty late. I told Mom I'd be home by one."

Between The Lines

Evelyn was not happy about running to the car in her formal, but I exhorted her on with Big Pink's orders. Eight and a half minutes later I had her at her doorstep.

"Well, goodnight," I said, offering her my hand.

She clasped my hand and looked from her scuffed shoes to the Big Boy sauce on my tux. "This has certainly been an evening to remember."

"Uh, yeah, I had a good time, too. G'night now!"

She took a step closer. "Aren't you forgetting something?"

"Oh, Yeah. Of course." I pulled out the photo that her dad had given me and held it up under the light next to her.

The freshness had long since worn off her, but she was still recognizable as the same girl.

"No dings, dents or scratches," I said. "And I'm returning you with a full tank. Want to initial it?"

"Yes, that's exactly what I want to do. Wait right here while I go inside and get a pen."

No sooner had she gone inside than the porch light went off. Girls were subtle creatures, Jimmy had said, and sometimes we needed to read between the lines for their signals. The sound of the door locking behind her, the house plunging into darkness – these were tiny clues that might have eluded the less skillful observer of the feminine condition, but not me. My evening was over.

I was soon in the safety and comfort of my own bedroom, and I wasted no time shedding my rental clothes, peeling them off as if they were on fire, and leaving them on the floor where they had fallen. Like a dog preparing for a nap, I turned round and round, trampling my tux until it no longer posed a threat.

Even though I was dog-tired and ready for bed, I first slipped into jeans and a T-shirt to decontaminate my body from the unwanted influences of formalwear. The denim and 100% cotton soothed my skin and restored my spirit. Clothes are like girls, I decided. It's always a good idea to get acquainted with them before committing to prolonged physical contact.

I flipped on the television in time to watch channel six go off the air. I stood briefly for the national anthem, then settled down into the pile of rental clothes and fell asleep.

Ahead of me lay sweet dreams of playing chess with Karen Kupchek, up by three pieces with excellent position.

"Did you hear about the two guys they found in White River last night?" she would say.

I would smile knowingly and move my bishop in for the kill.

prom redux

TWIRP Week

Midway between the end of basketball season and the Prom lurked the portentous TWIRP Week. Every other school in the Free World used the term Sadie Hawkins to describe this phenomenon, but at AHS we used TWIRP, an acronym for "The Woman Is Required to Pay," a wholly unappealing term which obviously went straight to market with no messy testing on focus groups. It was a time in which the locks on our social agreements were jimmied, and the girls were allowed, even encouraged, to unleash the latent predator within. And because their season lasted just one week each year, the girls entered it with religious fervor.

TWIRP Week culminated in the TWIRP Week Dance, a festival for the nouveau predators. The dance served two purposes. First, it was an opportunity for girls who already had Prom dates to say thanks for saving them from social ignominy. The second and more nefarious purpose was to give the girls with less sure social prospects a chance to go fishing. Many interpreted an acceptance to the TWIRP week dance as an implicit contract to reciprocate with a Prom invitation. These observations I made from the perspective of an outside observer, for I had always been safe from even the most desperate predators. I was safe, that is, until my senior year. "Desperate" is perhaps an uncharitable term, but if Brigitte Bardot had called me, I could have described *her* in no other way.

After years safely on the sidelines of the TWIRP Week action the phone call came as a monumental surprise.

"Hi, is this Bob?"

"Uh-huh..."

It was a girl, not Brigitte Bardot, but one whose voice was distantly familiar and pleasant. I scanned my memory banks but failed to match the voice with any of my female cousins.

"This is Evelyn. How are you?"

"Uh, fine." I was a scintillating conversationalist, especially under pressure.

"And you?" I quipped. Damn, I was good.

"Fine," she answered. Thrust, parry, thrust.

Where was all this leading? After the Prom and the Frisch's debacle, I knew it couldn't have been a social call.

"You know, the TWIRP Week Dance is coming up in about six weeks," she said.

"It is?"

The conversation had taken a threatening turn, and I did not like it. The bull was out of the gate, and there I stood in its path, dressed like Santa Claus. Besides, basketball season was still in full swing. Talk like this was out of season and maybe even prohibited.

"Yes," she continued. "It's on April tenth. I was wondering if you'd like to go with me."

"Hold on."

I put the phone down and ran to the kitchen, hoping Mom would save me.

"Mom, do I have anything going on April tenth?"

Surely there was impending oral surgery I had forgotten about, or maybe a seasonal illness that came around the first week of April each year. I wouldn't be that lucky, however. Mom confirmed that my calendar was open wide with possibility, just as it always was six weeks ahead.

I took a long breath and listened in amazement at the words that tumbled from my mouth.

"Sure, I'd love to."

It wasn't enough just to say, "Okay, I'll go." I had to say I'd *love* to. Had my use of the L-word activated the implied contract clause under the rules of engagement for the Prom? I made a note to myself to seek legal counsel before TWIRP Week. I also made a note to learn how to say *no*. I had never had an opportunity, much less a reason, to turn a girl down for anything. Yet, there I was, regretting that I could not spend the first weekend in April having impacted wisdom teeth crushed and removed from my jaw a sliver at a time, all under a local anesthetic that came and went, came and went.

There would be plenty of opportunities before the dance for me to entertain oral surgery fantasies. In the meantime though, there was basketball. The highlight was our annual triumph over Muncie Central and the ensuing commemorative fistfight, and soon we would be on our way to the state tournament.

We sailed through the sectionals, dismantling the small town teams up Highway 9 and out Highway 32 as a matter of course. Teams like these who found themselves on the sad end of an 83-41 score were charitably described in the newspapers as "scrappy." Our hopes for a championship disintegrated with a big loss in the regionals though, and the season would come to an end with another slide down the Big Glass Mountain. Our guys were sure scrappy in that last game though, and nobody could take that away from us.

The gloom of winter and defeat would soon give way to spring and the promise that it held. The first robins returned, and girls burst forth in revealing spring attire to test the limits of the dress code in schools everywhere. All was right with the world, and the thought of the TWIRP Week Dance looming ahead did nothing to dampen my spirits.

The dance was a semi-formal affair with no imminent tuxedo rental to haunt me. The same black J.C. Penney suit that I wore to church every Sunday would suffice for the dance, but my customary white socks would have to yield to something more appropriate. *Appropriate* was a word mothers used to bludgeon us into wearing clothes we hated. The appropriate socks would be found in Dad's dresser, and they came in two shades – *black as hell* and *despair*.

There would be no flowers for me to worry about either, and that was the best part of TWIRP Week. I could escape all the trials associated with a traditional dance, even the futility of driving a six-cylinder Rambler station wagon with a three-speed manual transmission. All that awaited me was the usual embarrassment on the dance floor, and so I chose to pretend that nothing lay ahead.

I preferred to consider my denial in Zen-like terms. I was merely living in the present moment. My strategy served me well, up until the final day, that is, when the present moment caught up with the Hour of Doom. There would be no oral surgery to save me, no convenient spring illness either. Nor was it going to be like a visit to the dentist, where I could hope to hide out in the waiting room and escape unnoticed.

Half an hour before the dance I was still in the bathtub, soaking in scalding hot water. I had watched Mom blanch tomatoes before, and I fully expected my skin to peel away when I toweled off. Burning pain filled me, leaving no room for conscious thought of the dance. Ah, the Zen of pain! First-degree burns were a small price to pay for inner peace. I cooled the water and sloshed it from end to end in the bathtub, imagining tidal waves that would sweep me out to sea until the dance was over. Brigitte Bardot would appear in a boat from out of nowhere to bring me a warm bathrobe, a dozen doughnuts, and a quart of chocolate milk with two straws.

Mom's knock on the door brought me back to shore, back to the present moment where a black suit with serious matching socks awaited me, as did a girl named Evelyn, a decent and upstanding citizen of Anderson High School whose only apparent personality flaw was liking me more than reason would dictate.

The next knock I heard was Evelyn's. She stood at the front door in anticipation. In her hands she held a carefully crafted bouquet of candy. I marveled at its perfection and considered with dread that its main ingredient was not sugar, but expectation.

Mom later said that when I left the house I looked as if I were being led to my execution, but it was worse than that. The guest of honor at an execution can always hold out a glimmer of hope that the governor will phone in a last minute pardon. I had no such hope. There are some things even a governor cannot pardon. Nonetheless, I listened for the telephone as Evelyn escorted me away from the safety and comfort of my home.

"Bob Deaton, this is the governor speaking. I've decided to commute your sentence to oral surgery. You are forthwith remanded to the custody of Dr. Boski."

"Thank you, Governor."

"Huh?"

"I mean 'Thank you, Evelyn. Thank you for the lovely edible bouquet.'"

She beamed with pride and led me off to her waiting car. I resolved to raise no hope and make no promise, explicit or implicit, through word, deed or action that would suggest I would be at the Prom as someone's date or as a disinterested observer. Should the Prom arise in conversation, I would immediately change the subject to Maury Wills' attempt to break Ty Cobb's record of ninety-six stolen bases in a single season.

I recall nothing that happened after that. Nothing about the dance or where we went afterward, nothing about what I did with the candy corsage while we danced or whether Evelyn thought Maury Wills had a shot. There was a brief hug at the doorstep – that much I recall – and with it a feeling that a burden had been lifted.

Earning The Stamp Of Approval

"Hey…"

A desperate tone infected Jimmy's voice.

"Hey," I responded. It was an elaborate protocol we had developed over the years.

"So, have you asked Evelyn to the Prom yet?"

"Haven't we plowed this row already? I'm not going to the Prom. And if I'm not going to the Prom, I'm not going with Evelyn."

"C'mon! You know you're going! Everybody goes. You gotta ask her! It's getting late!"

"Late? What is it? Five, six weeks away?"

How late could it be? There was still uneaten candy on my TWIRP Week bouquet.

"Annie says it's late. And if Annie says it's late, it's late."

It was a strange calendar that girls kept. Anything beyond my next haircut was long-range planning, and long-range planning was not an arrow in my quiver. I was good for one, maybe two haircuts before the Prom.

"Annie's not happy, Bob. Evelyn's her best friend, and she doesn't have a Prom date. And if Annie's not happy, you know what that makes me?"

"A spineless tool whose sole reason for being is to satisfy his girlfriend's every wish, no matter how unreasonable?"

That was easy for me to say. I had no girlfriend, and my prospects were poor for the remainder of the century.

'C'mon, Bob! I can't take the heat! Evelyn needs a date, and if she doesn't go with you, who's she going to go with?"

"Look, no more formal dances for me with Evelyn or anybody else. Nothing personal." I knew then that I would never run for president, if only to avoid the inaugural ball.

"Think about it," he said. "Look deep into your soul, think about what's right and do it!"

"I'm looking. I'm thinking. I'm not going."

"Look deeper. Think harder." He breathed a deep sigh and hung up.

Desperation was a cheap commodity this time of year.

Every day for the next two weeks, Jimmy and I ran through some variation of the same conversation with the same results. Then one day, there was no call. Had he given up on me? Had Annie dumped him in disgust? Had he disguised his voice as mine and asked Evelyn himself? In a pre-emptive strike I dialed his number.

"Hey."

"Hey."

"You didn't call me today. I was missing the pressure."

"No pressure now. I've got Plan B."

"Plan B?"

"Yep, *B* as in Basil. Basil's going to take her."

"Our friend Basil? The innocent and unsuspecting foreign exchange student far from his home in the Middle East entrusted to our care? How? Why?"

"I told him that the State Department would find out he didn't go to the Prom, and they'd stamp his passport *Socially Undesirable*."

"Surely he didn't buy that."

"No, he didn't. It was too subtle. So, I explained that the stamp meant he didn't like girls all that much."

"Are you serious? You told Basil that?"

"Nah. Didn't have to. He was just as easy as you were last year. Peace has been restored. Evelyn's happy, Annie's happy, and now I'm happy."

"Hey, I'm happy, too."

"Hmm, that's nice, but you really didn't figure into my equation."

"And what about your innocent pawn Basil? I think you need to look deep into your soul and think hard about what you've done."

"I'm looking. I'm thinking. I'm hanging up now."

A couple of weeks passed and the lure of the Prom began to work its ways with me. The nature of its lure was not at all obvious. God knows the music was awful, and the dancing was a painful exercise in self-consciousness. Even in the darkness surrounded by five hundred classmates, many of the boys as inept as I, I felt as if I'd shown up naked at my own graduation. Wearing a tuxedo was like being strapped into a rusty, sharp-edged mechanism of torture in the downstairs rec room of a medieval castle. Girls had been confined to all manner of straps and harnesses from the time the goddess of puberty had smiled upon them, and they were used to it, but it was not a habit to which I intended to become accustomed. And yet, there was something compelling about it for all of us. Everybody did it because everybody else did it. The Prom was the most convincing argument against free will that one could make.

And so, knowing that Saturday was a slow TV night on all three channels, I crumbled. I fell into the orbit of the Prom, and from that, there would be no escape. I could at least rest easy knowing that beneath the "Corrective lenses required" warning on my driver license, the Indiana Department of Motor Vehicles would not enter the stamp of shame, *Socially Undesirable.*

Encore

Christine was an old friend from the days when I was better at bed-wetting than tying my shoes. She was engaged to be married in June, but her fiancé would not be permitted to take his bride-to-be to the most important social engagement of the year. He was a "Prom alien." He was not an eleventh or twelfth grade male at AHS. Not like me.

Christine was a fellow traveler on the road of ambivalence. She shared my compulsion to go, just as one feels compelled to slow down to stare at an auto accident. She also shared my lack of enthusiasm for the idea of spending an evening bound and flowered and immersed in generic music. It was a natural match, and with little discussion we agreed to go. Because of her engagement status, it could not in the remotest sense be considered a date. Instead, we were co-dependents, willing props in each other's Ken and Barbie Prom set, no different from a cummerbund or nosegay. Such was the lure of the Prom that a woman on the brink of marriage would go to the biggest dance of the year with someone not her fiancé. And such was the extent of my geekiness that her fiancé would not feel a single moment of unease about our arrangement.

As fate would have it, we were the third leg of a triple date. We went in Jimmy's '58 Pontiac convertible, a machine

dubbed "The Great White Bird" by a local cop who appre-
hended him shortly after takeoff at a stoplight a block from
Frisch's downtown. The rich aroma of its leather seats com-
peted with the riot of scents emanating from its freshly
scrubbed occupants. Basil and I sat in the back, borne on the
waves of taffeta pouring forth from Christine and Evelyn's
gowns. Jimmy was behind the wheel with Annie close by, and
the pheromones oozing from their every pore washed over us
with no effect. Personal histories were set aside, and Evelyn
was cheerfully impervious to my presence.

In the back of The Great White Bird no hard feelings
were to be found among us as we strutted and fretted our
hour upon the stage. At the end of the evening each of us
silently and solemnly looked deep into our respective souls
and thought hard about what we had done. And we were
glad.

epilogue

A few short weeks after the Prom we found ourselves back in the gym sweating in funny costumes for one more production, the one they called Commencement. The orchestra relentlessly ground out strains of *Pomp and Circumstance* to fill the June night air, as we sweltered in our gowns and caps. At the sound of our names, each of the 641 members of my graduating class scrambled onto the stage to receive a handshake from the principal and a personalized certificate of endurance. Our supporting cast in the bleachers beamed down on us with pride and pondered what our futures may hold. We on the floor pondered the parties that would begin right after Zigfield, Steven L received his diploma. Our long-term view of the future went out about three months. We were, after all, the ones who had inscribed the yearbooks of countless classmates we would never see again with wishes to "Have a great summer!"

Anderson was a marvelous small town Petri dish in which we had grown and flourished like bacteria. In the months after graduation some of us would go off to college. Others would see Viet Nam. Some would disparage Anderson as a hick town where there was nothing to do and move to the big city where they would watch the same TV shows and drive twice as far to the same franchise coffee shops. Others hung around and disproved the notion that there was nothing to do by inadvertently making one baby after another. My class made sure that the Wednesday night wedding industry and the maternity ward at St John's continued to thrive. Those that followed us ensured the continued success of Frisch's on Broadway, and we all shared one thing in common. We couldn't see past Saturday night.

And it was good. Real good.